OPPORTUNITIES IN

METEOROLOGY

by Miles F. Harris

Produced with the cooperation
of the American Meteorological Society

Vocational Guidance Manuals

EDUCATIONAL BOOKS DIVISION OF
UNIVERSAL PUBLISHING AND DISTRIBUTING CORPORATION
NEW YORK

VOCATIONAL GUIDANCE MANUALS
Published by Universal Publishing and
Distributing Corporation
235 East 45th Street
New York, N. Y. 10017

Revised Edition

Manufactured in the
United States of America

ABOUT THE AUTHOR

MILES F. HARRIS has worked in meteorology since he entered the U.S. Weather Bureau at Macon, Ga., in 1932, except for a brief tour in the U.S. Merchant Marine. Upon his retirement from the Environmental Science Services Administration, U.S. Department of Commerce, in 1971, he joined the staff of the American Meteorological Society as Technical Editor of the *Bulletin of the AMS* and Special Projects Officer.

During his civil service career, Mr. Harris worked successively as a weather observer, weather analyst, forecaster, research meteorologist, and editor. He spent most of his government career in Washington, D.C. He also served at weather offices in Savannah, Ga., Chattanooga, Tenn., and San Juan, P.R. He received a Bachelor of Science degree in meteorology from New York University in 1944. In 1955, he returned to N.Y.U. for a year and in 1957 received an M.S. in meteorology from that university.

Mr. Harris has written two popular books about meteorology and the work of meteorological organizations. These appeared in a young peoples' series that provides background information about challenging work in science, social service, and other fields. During the summers of 1964-66, he worked at Boulder, Colo., with the Earth Science Curriculum Project. This project, sponsored by the American Geological Institute with support from the National Science Foundation, produced a textbook in the earth sciences.

The author has also contributed scientific articles to such journals as the *Monthly Weather Review*, the *Journal of Atmospheric Sciences*, and the *Journal of Geophysical Research*. His research interest, at the time he was active in research, was in the atmosphere's diurnal variations, collectively described as the atmospheric tides. At the time of his retirement from civil service, Mr. Harris was Editor of the *Monthly Weather Review*.

FOREWORD

THE WEATHER is an intimate part of our daily lives, and for this reason most people have more than a passing interest in meteorology. This was particularly true of my generation, most of whom grew up either in small cities or towns, if not in the open country where one could watch the weather as it approached miles away. Then many of us moved to big cities or to the expanding suburbs to live and work in climatically conditioned houses and offices, to travel in air-conditioned automobiles or buses, and to spend most of our adult lives much more carefully protected from the discomforts of weather. Many people lost the vital concern with weather that earlier generations were never privileged to forget.

When weather satellites made it possible for us to "see" much of the world's weather on our television screens—to the extent that weather is represented by the cloud systems of great storms—many young people again became amateur weathermen and amateur meteorologists. More recently, many others have been stimulated to renewed interest in the atmosphere by an increasing public awareness of the many disadvantages and the occasional hazards of air pollution.

To those young people whose interest in the atmosphere is

more than a casual one, meteorology offers a challenging field for professional and paraprofessional careers.

Although both popular and professional interest in the atmosphere has been stimulated by the developments of the space age and by social pressures to conserve and improve the quality of our environment, meteorology embraces many other vital areas of activity. Indeed, the applications of meteorology to man and his society are too complex and far-reaching for any one individual to master. Similarly, meteorology's interactions with other disciplines and professions appear to be almost endless. The great variety inherent in meteorology—in its applications and in its ties with other disciplines—invites the talents of individuals of widely varying interests and skills.

The profession of meteorology has grown rapidly during the past two decades. The 1950s and the 1960s witnessed great advances both in theoretical and practical meteorology.

Perhaps more than most sciences, meteorology benefited almost immediately from the post-World War II advances in computing science, communications technology, and the ventures into space. Many theoretical barriers were pushed forward, but these achievements also opened up new frontiers. There are many fundamental problems in meteorology waiting to be solved, and challlenging opportunities await the creative young scientist who is interested in theoretical work.

There is currently an expectation among meteorologists that during the coming decades it will be in the application of the science to social needs that meteorology will see its greatest expansion in terms of numbers of practitioners. Ordinarily, the applications of a science require many more people than were required to produce the basic research that makes professional services feasible.

In recent decades, many career opportunities in meteorology

were provided by the applications of computers, improved communications techniques, and satellites to weather forecasting and research. Because meteorology is a strongly service-directed science, theoretical advances were put rapidly into practice, creating new careers for applied scientists and technicians.

As a result of advances along both fronts, theoretical and applied, the scientific and technological bases for an extension of meteorological services now exist. Public and private needs for expanded meteorological services also exist. Better warnings of storms and floods, in combination with education about the weather and its ways, could save many lives and reduce human suffering in this country and abroad. The current emphasis on the environment reminds meteorologists that they have had little actual input into urban planning and industrial siting. Meteorology also has much to contribute to human health and recreation; to agriculture, forestry, and ecology; and to utilities, transportation, construction, marketing, and other commercial areas. As the needs of our society change, it is probable that the emphasis in meterological training and in meteorological careers will change also.

In the following pages, Mr. Harris makes the point that meteorology is unique among the sciences in that two-thirds of the profession are directly employed by the federal government, either in civilian or in military capacities. Many other meteorologists receive financial support for their work either indirectly or directly from the government. As a result, year-to-year employment in meteorology is closely related to federal science policies and funding. However, looking farther ahead, meteorologists are reasonably confident in the continued growth of their profession. This confidence is based ultimately on an understanding of the close application of meteorology to human needs. Meteorological requirements and services are deeply woven into the social fabric, not only of nations but of the world community.

The American Meteorological Society recognizes a current
need for more comprehensive information about careers in
meteorology. High school guidance counselors and the students
whom they advise should find this book particularly useful. The
book has also been written with the university student in mind
who has already elected meteorology as a major subject and is
faced with the problem of getting a job. Employers or prospective employers of meteorologists may also find parts of it of
practical interest. It is with much personal satisfaction that I
commend the book to their attention.

> *Kenneth C. Spengler*
> *Executive Director,*
> *American Meteorological*
> *Society*

ACKNOWLEDGMENTS

THE AUTHOR wishes to express his appreciation to the Executive Committee of the American Meteorological Society for making it possible for him to complete this book under the Society's sponsorship; to Messrs. John R. Gerhardt and Matthew Toyli of the Society's headquarters staff for their advice and encouragement; and to Mr. George Hatzenbuhler of the National Oceanic and Atmospheric Administration, Mr. Albert V. Carlin of the University of Rhode Island, and Mr. Victor E. McCrory of the National Weather Service for their valuable help in getting the book under way.

He would also like to thank Dr. Werner A. Baum, President of the University of Rhode Island, for permission to quote at length from his article on meteorological education in the United States; Admiral William J. Kotsch, Commander of the Naval Weather Service, for information about Navy weather careers; Mr. John D. Rugg, Information Officer, Air Weather Service, for materials on weather activities and careers in the Air Force; and Mr. James L. Dicke, NOAA meteorologist, Environmental Protection Agency, for information about career opportunities in the field of environmental protection and control.

For their help in reviewing the manuscript, the author is grateful to the following individuals: Mr. Eugene Bollay, immeidate Past President, American Meteorological Society; Prof. James E. Miller, Chairman, Department of Meteorology and Oceanography, New York University; and Chairman, Board of Meteorological Education in Universities, American Meteorological Society; Mr. John D. Rugg, Air Weather Service; Mrs. Muriel D. Christgau and Messrs. George Hatzenbuhler and Clyde Hughes, National Oceanic and Atmospheric Administration; and Mr. John R. Gerhardt, Associate Director for Education, and Mrs. Karen Reixach, American Meteorological Society.

CONTENTS

TABLES

FIGURES

CHAPTER 1

CAREERS IN METEOROLOGY

SINCE YOU HAVE OPENED this book, the chances are that you are toying, more or less seriously, with the idea of making a career of meteorology, or that you are advising someone who is interested in a meteorological career. If so, you are looking for answers to many specific questions. For example, what do meteorologists do? What kind of education do you need to become one? Do meteorologists make a good living, commensurate with the time, effort, and expense necessary in preparing for a career? Who employs meteorologists? Is it possible to work and prepare for a professional career at the same time?

It is the aim of this book to answer these and other specific questions about careers in meteorology, and also to convey something of the more intangible aspects of a career in this relatively small but expanding field. There are, of course, many other persons whom the student may wish to consult in deciding whether or not to pick meteorology as a career: his school guidance counselor, who is skilled in matching potentialities to the varied requirements of many fields; his teachers, who from daily contact with hundreds of students may have a good insight into his unique capacities as an individual; his family, who probably have their own ideas for his future; and his friends, and friends of friends, among whom he may find one who is a meteorologist or who is working in a closely related field. For the present, let's see what meteorology is, and what it is not.

WHAT IS METEOROLOGY?

WHEN MOST PEOPLE think of meteorology, they have a mental picture of a television announcer summarizing the weather over the country and presenting the local forecast for the next day or so. Yet not all TV weathermen are meteorologists, nor are all meteorologists weather forecasters. Of the approximately 7,000 professional meteorologits now working in the United States, only about a third are primarily concerned with weather forecasting. Meteorology and weather forecasting are not synonymous.

Weather forecasting is a technical skill, like navigation, or like searching for oil and other minerals, or mapping the Earth's surface, charting the ocean's currents, predicting the tides, considering the effects of earthquakes on buildings, or predicting the orbit of a satellite. Just as one needs to be a geologist to search intelligently for oil, and an expert in one or more of the other sciences to prescribe techniques of navigation, predict the tides, or bring an astronaut safely home to earth, so a weather forecaster needs to be trained in the science of meteorology. Thus, meteorology is a science, while weather forecasting is the meteorological skill with which the general public happens to be most familiar. It is one of the many applications of meteorology to man's needs.

Perhaps it has occurred to you that all of the technical skills mentioned above have something in common. They are all concerned, in one way or another, with the problem of making it possible for men to carry on their activities safely and effectively within their environment—whether it be on land, sea, air, or somewhere at the edges of the atmosphere or in space. Thus, the sciences on which these skills depend have come to be called the *environmental sciences.* Perhaps it is a sign of the youth and vigor of these scientific disciplines that it is hard to find a collective name on which everyone agrees, and they are frequently referred to as the geophysical sciences, Earth sciences, or planetary and space sciences. These are sciences of the physical environment. The term *environmental sciences* also embraces ecology, which is concerned with the interrelationship between living organisms and the physical environment.

Meteorology is the environmental science that is concerned with the study of atmospheres—usually the Earth's atmosphere, but also the atmospheres of other planets. Like its sister sciences—oceanography, geology, geodesy, geomagnetism, astronomy, and their various branches—meteorology applies the laws of physics, chemistry, biology, and mathematics to the study of a portion of our physical environment. In particular, meteorology seeks to describe, understand, predict, and, where possible, to exercise some measure of control over the atmosphere—its composition, including water vapor, cloud, dust, and smog; its swift and violent changes, manifest in tornadoes, hurricanes, blizzards, and cold waves; and its longer, cyclic changes alternating between drought and flooding rains. Meteorology is synonymous with *atmospheric science,* a term that has come into common usage in recent years.

Because the atmosphere itself is complex and because its effects on man and his activities are varied and widespread, meteorology is an unusually rich field in which to work and study. Although its history traces backward in time to the ancient Greeks, it is a young and vital study nevertheless—because the twentieth century has brought many new tools—radio, radar, lidar, aircraft, rockets, satellites, and electronic computers—that make it possible to explore the atmosphere more effectively. With new observations and computing tools have come powerful new ways of applying the laws of physics and mathematics to the study of the atmosphere, to weather forecasting, and to other uses of the science.

At the same time that new observations and new techniques are strengthening meteorology as a science, new services are being demanded of it. Contemporary problems like air pollution, the contamination of the atmosphere with radioactive materials, and the diminishing supply of food for the world's rapidly growing populations require meteorologists to help solve them. Complex defense systems, jet aircraft, rockets, and satellites have all brought new requirements for weather information. For some years, meteorologists have been planning for the weather needs of commercial supersonic travel, and more recently they have been called upon to evaluate the potential effects of the supersonic transport on the atmosphere. Simply because the atmosphere is our natural habitat, almost every new activity or technological development makes a new demand on meteorology; and some of them create new areas of specialization in the profession.

The air is our natural element, and the atmosphere is the receptacle of all of our gaseous wastes, in addition to many solid products of combustion. Materials released high in the atmosphere are widely diffused; like the ocean, the atmosphere is the common property of all mankind. Meteorology is preeminently an international science.

CAREER AREAS AND SPECIALIZATION

BROADLY SPEAKING, meteorologists may be classed as teachers, research meteorologists, and operational and service meteorologists. A fourth category might be called engineering meteorologists, those concerned with the design of instruments and with the effects of the atmosphere on structures and materials. There are no rigid walls between these career areas of meteorology. Indeed, more often than not, university teachers of meteorology pursue their own research or supervise research projects under grants or contracts from government agencies. Similarly, operational meteorologists who provide the nation's weather observing, forecasting, and other public or specialized services often produce research. Undeniably, however, the wider support of science by government during the past two decades has made it possible for more and more meteorologists to regard themselves exclusively as research scientists without teaching or operational responsibilities.

In 1970, about 25 percent of the professional meteorologists* who responded to a government survey of scientific manpower [1] listed research or its administration as their primary duty; 7 percent listed teaching; while nearly all of the remaining 68 percent were concerned with the operational and service aspects of meteorology. By far the greater portion of the latter group were involved with the operation and management of the nation's basic and specialized weather systems, civilian and military.

Thus, about one-fourth of the nation's meteorologists are occupied in providing new ideas, knowledge, and techniques

---

*Listed as "atmospheric and space scientists" in the survey, but essentially the same group designated "meteorologists" in earlier surveys.

for application of the science; another fifth are primarily concerned with the business of running weather systems and offices; almost half are operating meteorologists actively engaged in analyzing weather data, preparing forecasts, answering requests for information and advice, and similar duties; while only a few—less than one in ten—count it their main responsibility to educate future meteorologists.

With the development of novel ways of observing the atmosphere and with expanding requirements for weather information, new fields of specialization are continually opening up in meteorology. These new developments often begin in response to a need in operations and services but then stimulate research and teaching, as well. Not many years ago, three or four specialties adequately described the science: *physical, dynamic,* and *synoptic meteorology,* and *climatology. Physical meteorology* deals with the composition of the atmosphere, with radiative processes, optical phenomena, lightning, the nature and formation of cloud and rain drops, and the like. *Dynamic meteorology* deals with the motions of the atmosphere and the forces and energy changes involved. *Synoptic meteorology* developed from the study of the weather map—*synoptic* means "single-view"—and is concerned mainly with the analysis of the weather in order to describe and explain, or to forecast, weather developments. *Climatology,* sometimes regarded as a separate discipline, is the branch of meteorology that deals with the weather over a period of time; like weather forecasting, climatology has many applications to human affairs.

To these broad categories may be added many relatively new specialties, the more important ones being listed in Table 1 (Chapter 3, page 51). These specialties are created by the complexity of the science itself and by its many applications in other fields. Because of these applications, meteorology may be fruitfully combined with other fields in preparation for interesting interdisciplinary careers. Among these other fields are environmental engineering (e.g., air pollution control), environmental management, biology, environmental health, civil engineering (e.g., hydrometeorology), electrical engineering (e.g., instrumentation), oceanography, astronomy, geology, aerospace engineering, mathematics (e.g., mathematical modelling, computer programing), and agriculture. The opportunities for specialization will be made clear later as we discuss the duties of meteorologists working in various career areas.

WHO EMPLOYS METEOROLOGISTS?

METEOROLOGICAL SERVICES require networks of observation stations, both on the national and international scales, and the means to collect reports quickly and efficiently. Moreover, weather and climatological services are necessary to the safety and well-being of the general public, to the national defense, and to important parts of the economy like aviation, shipping, and agriculture. For these reasons, basic meteorological responsibilities are universally recognized to be the responsibility of governments. At the same time, some highly specialized needs of individuals, business, and industry are not considered, in the United States, to be the government's function. To meet these quite specialized needs, some industries employ their own meteorologists, while others use the services of the many consulting firms that have grown up in the United States since the close of World War II. Formal education in meteorology is the concern of universities and colleges, although specialized training programs are carried out by the larger meteorological employers.

The federal government, including civilian agencies and the military services, is by far the largest employer of meteorologists in the United States. In 1970, 32 percent of the professional meteorologists responding to a manpower survey were on active duty with the military services and 31 percent were civilian employees of the federal government. Fifteen percent were employed by educational institutions, 12 percent by industry and local governments, and one percent were self-employed. The very small percentage of self-employed meteorologists perhaps reflects the fact that even the private practice of meteorology requires a small staff of experts organized into a consulting firm.

The basic weather system of the United States' meteorological service is the responsibility of the National Oceanic and Atmospheric Administration (NOAA), which includes the National Weather Service, the National Environmental Satellite Service, the Environmental Data Service, and the Environmental Research Laboratories, to name only those units concerned with meteorology. All of these components of NOAA employ large numbers of meteorologists, accounting for all but a small percentage of those employed by civilian agencies. NOAA's National Ocean Survey includes most of the agency's Commissioned Corps, many of whom are trained in meteorology as well as in geodesy, oceanography, and other disciplines of the geophysical sciences. Other federal agencies employing civilian meteorologists are the National Aeronautics and Space Administration, the Federal Aviation Administration, the Environmental Protection Agency, the Defense Department, the Atomic Energy Commission, the Department of Agriculture, and the Department of the Interior. As Federal Coordinator for Meteorological Services and Supporting Research, the Administrator of NOAA is responsible for coordinating the meteorological activities of the civilian and military services of the federal government.

Meteorologists in the military services are largely concentrated in the Air Weather Service of the U.S. Air Force and the Naval Weather Service of the U.S. Navy.

Throughout government, professional meteorologists are aided by nonprofessional or paraprofessional employees. It was estimated in 1971 that there were about 7,500 individuals working as professional meteorologists or atmospheric scientists in the United States or in the Armed Forces overseas. For every professional, there are roughly two paraprofessionals who work as technicians, weather observers, weather briefers, airman forecasters, officials in charge of weather stations, and at similar duties. The total figure of 22,500 meteorological personnel—professional and nonprofessional—was based on manpower survey results in 1970 and on data obtained from the larger employers of meteorologists. This brings us to another point—the differences between and the differing requirements for professional and nonprofessional careers.

PROFESSIONAL AND NONPROFESSIONAL CAREERS

IN THE CIVILIAN AGENCIES, educational requirements for passage from the "ranks" to professional status have varied with the demands for services and the supply of professional meteorologists. Early in the 1950s, for example, candidates for the position of meteorologist were required to have either a bachelor's degree in meteorology; or four years of progressive professional experience in meteorology (which might well have been acquired without benefit of a degree in meteorology, since before 1940 there were few opportunities to obtain a dagree in the field); or an equivalent combination of academic training and professional experience.

In 1968, the Weather Bureau (now the National Weather Service), redefined and clarified its policy on nonprofessional and professional duties and careers. The new policy distinguishes more clearly than before between the jobs of meteorologist and meteorological technician. It also opens up new careers for the technician, since the officials in charge of a large number of the Weather Service's field offices, called General Weather Service Offices, are now classified as technicians. In general, meteorological technicians are required to be high school graduates, while newly entering meteorologists are required to have college degrees. In the military services, weather officers must hold a bachelor's degree (preferably in science or engineering) and complete a prescribed meteorology program. Enlisted personnel may advance to positions of considerable responsibility and may become commissioned officers on the completion of a college degree prgram and Officers Training School. Essentially, the duties of technicians require the same degree of skill, training, and ability among the civilian and military services; this is also true of the duties of meteorologists.

The renewed emphasis on formal educational requirements is primarily a result of the expansion of research, the establishment of meteorology on a sounder scientific basis, and the more extensive application of scientific method to weather forecasting and other operations and services. In 1963, the American Meteorological Society altered its constitution to require that new applicants for professional membership have degrees in meteorology, climatology, or a related discipline, and be active contributors to the development of the science or application of meteorology. Prior to that date, applicants who had been engaged in professional work for a period of five years were accepted for professional membership.

Thus, although there are today a number of professional

meteorologists who have not attained the bachelor's degree, the opportunity for becoming a meteorologist without formal academic training is essentially a thing of the past.

EDUCATION AND TRAINING

WHETHER A STUDENT'S immediate objective is to become a meteorologist or a meteorological technician, his high school preparation should include courses in physics, chemistry, and mathematics. Although more and more high schools are offering some meteorology as part of Earth science courses, the student aiming at a career in meteorology should regard Earth science as a valuable supplement to but not a susbtitute for physics or chemistry. If he plans to continue his education after high school, he should, of course, satisfy the general requirements for college entrance.

In choosing a college and planning his further education, the prospective meteorologist will have wider choices and more options. It is at this point that he should begin to think seriously about the kind of career he wants and thinks himself capable of achieving, whether in operations and services, research, teaching, or engineering. There is some difference of opinion among educators as to what constitutes the best approach to a meteorological education. Some educators regard meteorology as essentially a graduate study, holding that the undergraduate years should be devoted to a sound preparation in the physical sciences and mathematics. Others feel that certain *advanced* courses, say in physics, that might be required for an undergraduate degree have little relevance to meteorology. Some universities offer graduate, but not undergraduate, degrees in meteorology. Fortunately, there is enough diversity among the 50 or more North

American universities offering meteorology to permit a choice based on the student's own professional objectives and resources. In the United States, about 38 institutions offer the bachelor's degree in meteorology or a closely related field, while 51 offer advanced degrees.

Both NOAA and the military services have programs under which they send appreciable numbers of promising employees to universities for education at the advanced level, with full financial support. The operating agencies also assist their employees in other ways to obtain formal training in areas connected with their duties. At the universities, teaching and research assistantships offer financial security to graduate students. From the practical, financial point of view, the biggest hurdle facing the prospective meteorologist, whatever his ultimate objective, is the bachelor's degree. Having completed his undergraduate requirements, the chances are good that he can find support for graduate work, provided he is qualified.

EARNINGS OF METEOROLOGISTS

AS IN OTHER PROFESSIONS, a number of factors determine the earnings of meteorologists: ability, education and experience, the employer, and the law of supply and demand. Based on figures gathered in 1970, the median salary of civilian atmospheric and space scientists was $15,200, compared with $15,000 for all scientific and technical fields covered by the survey. (The median is the middle number of a series; that is, half the meteorologists surveyed made more; and half less than $15,200.) However, meteorologists with the Ph.D. had a median salary of $17,600, compared with $16,500 for all fields. In Chapter 8, you will find additional statistics on the earnings of meteorologists according to education, employment, and skills.

The median salary of meteorological technicians in civilian government jobs in 1970 was estimated at $10,000, and salaries ranged from $5,524 to approximately $15,000.

EMPLOYMENT OUTLOOK

THE DEMAND for well-trained meteorologists has usually exceeded the supply from the mid-1950s onward. In 1971, there was some unemployment among meteorologists (2.7 percent), but the profession was much better off than some other scientific fields. For example, among physicists, the unemployment rate was 3.9, and other fields also were experiencing the effects of recession and curtailment of government spending in science and technology. In the federal government, the Civil Service Commission permits meteorologists entering certain grades to be paid at higher rates, within their salary range, than the initial rate. On the average, opportunities for employment are probably roughly proportional to the numbers of meteorologists employed in each area, although the turnover rate is evidently somewhat greater in the military services than among other employers. On this assumption, career opportunities are most numerous in the military and civilian services of the federal government, in the universities, and in business and industry, in that order.

About 80 percent of employed meteorologists owe their jobs to the federal government, either directly through employment or through contracts and grants. Employment opportunities in meteorology thus fluctuate with the political climate and with the allocation of priorities in the federal budget.

In 1971, it was estimated that about 500 new meteorologists

obtained jobs, either replacing those leaving the profession or retiring, or filling newly created positions. These figures are based on the actual requirements of some employers and on what are considered to be conservative estimates of the requirements of others. A number of known conditions makes it reasonable to predict, in the long run, a continued and growing demand for meteorologists.

The science itself is in a state of rapid development, almost revolutionary in nature, as a result of increased theoretical activity during the past few decades, new technology, and an increasing demand for environmental information. Our complex society needs more and more highly detailed meteorological data, particularly more accurate forecasts for all practicable time periods. Much more data are needed for the control of air pollution and for the prevention of unwanted, man-made effects on local climates. Better ways of disseminating warnings of severe weather are needed for the protection of a population that year by year becomes more vulnerable because of increased settlement and exposure to hurricanes, storm surges, floods, and severe local storms. Finally, it is a matter of fact that a very large number of the professional meteorologists now working (1970) were trained as a single group during the early years of World War II. Most of this group will be retiring in the 1970s, so that employment should rise somewhat during the decade to replace those retirees (Chapter 8).

PERSONAL QUALIFICATIONS

SINCE METEOROLOGY is a science, the attributes of a scientist are naturally the most valuable for a successful career in the field: an inquiring mind, imagination, and creative ability, combined with the capacity to recognize facts and analyze them objectively. The research scientist needs also to be able to organize the results of his investigations for effective presentation at meetings and in scientific articles. As in any field, the good teacher of meteorology has a grasp of the field, verbal skills, and the enthusiasm to inspire his students.

Operational and service meteorologists need the ability to work closely with others, the poise to perform well under emergency situations, deadlines, and schedules, and, in many cases, the stamina to work rotating shifts at field stations and forecast centers. A strong sense of responsibility is an important attribute of the many workers in meteorology whose duties frequently, sometimes routinely, affect the public safety. Meteorology is a round-the-clock, round-the-world operation. Some meteorologists and technicians serve on Pacific islands, in the Arctic and Antarctic, on weather ships, on weather reconnaissance aircraft, and on oceanographic expeditions, so the ability to adapt to unusual living conditions is an occasional requirement. Although different career areas call for somewhat different skills and capabilities, underlying most successful careers in meteorology is a genuine interest in the atmosphere and its ways—an interest not difficult to cultivate—and a readiness to meet its challenges.

REFERENCES

1. National Science Foundation. *American Science Manpower* 1970, *A Report of the National Register of Scientific and Technical Personnel.* Washington, D.C.: National Science Foundation, 1972.

CHAPTER 2

THE CHALLENGE OF METEOROLOGY

THE STORY is told that President Lincoln, when he was approached by a weatherman with a plan for starting a weather service for the armies of the Republic, refused to see the man a second time because he had predicted fair weather, and rain was coming down. Indeed, for many years the profession of practicing meteorologist does not seem to have been an enviable one. Jocular names were given to weathermen, such as "weather wizard," "weather sharp," and "Old Prob." This was a period when the meteorologist as scientist and the meteorologist as weather forecaster pursued their separate ways. Hardly more than 50 years ago these ways began to converge, and there are signs that they are now meeting. Today, weather forecasting in middle and higher latitudes is based essentially on scientific methods, and the forecasts are measurably better than they were 20 years ago. This is not to say that the forecasts are perfect—far from it! Indeed, if they were, you might conclude that all of the problems are solved, and be tempted to seek a more challenging profession!

In the fields of scientific endeavor, it is possible to arrive either too early or too late to take part in the revolutionary advances. No future Newton will discover the universal law of gravitation; nor would it be reasonable to believe that Newton himself could have formulated the law had not Kepler, before him, so carefully analyzed the motions of the planets. At any particular time, certain areas of science are more attractive than others simply because those areas are in their "golden age" of development while others are nearly dormant, awaiting a new surge of discovery and activity. There are many indications that the geophysical sciences, supported by new tools for observation, exploration, and analysis, are in a revolutionary stage today. Their strictly scientific potentialities are, moreover, matched by practical necessities. Never before has man's need to understand, conserve, and control his physical environment been more pressing—simply because he is now making greater use of that environment than ever before. Only within the past few years has the importance of the physical environment to man's survival come to be realized by the man in the street.

In this chapter, we consider meteorology in historical perspective and as a science. What opportunities does meteorology hold for scientific accomplishment? What does it offer those individuals who feel an urge to make lasting contributions to knowledge and to society? For many individuals, these are important considerations in choosing a career.

METEOROLOGY AND SOCIETY

UNDOUBTEDLY, MAN'S CONCERN with the atmosphere predates civilization. Primitive man must have cowered at the thunder and fled from forest fires set by lightning. With

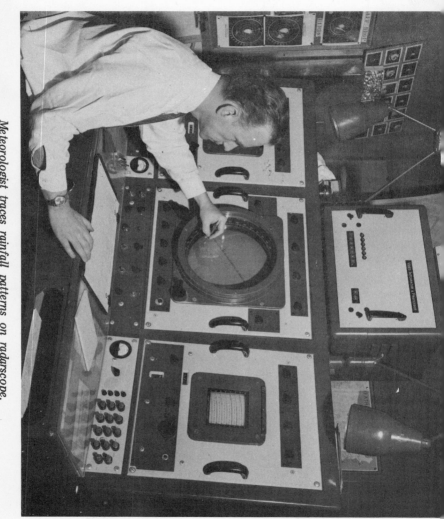

Meteorologist traces rainfall patterns on radarscope.
Courtesy of ESSA

magic and incantation, he must have sought power over the elements that sometimes endangered his existence. His ancestors may have developed flesh-eating habits when climatic changes forced them to desert drought-stricken vegetation, which yielded fewer and fewer berries, nuts, and fruits, and to become hunters.

It appears that advanced civilizations developed first in areas that were nearly independent of weather—notably in Egypt, whose prosperity depended upon the annual rise of the Nile and on irrigation. Although Egyptian sailors must have learned a great deal about the winds and weather of the Mediterranean, Egyptian farmers were not concerned with the vagaries of the weather. Water came from hundreds of miles away, where tropical rains were not interrupted by serious drought. To the north, in Greece, where civilization developed later, weather was more important, and it is here that meteorology had its early beginnings. Here, too, early attempts at weather control were made in the form of sacrifices to the gods, at whose pleasure the rain, the winds, and the storms were believed to come. Zeus, the ruler of the skies, commanded a host of lesser deities who personified the phenomena of the atmosphere.

However, the Greeks were a practical and rational people, and by the fifth century B.C. they began to make systematic weather observations, which were publicly displayed for the information of the townsmen and farmers. They invented a wind vane and various kinds of rain gauges. In the fourth century B.C., Aristotle wrote his monumental treatise, the *Meteorologica,* that gave the science its name. Although many of Aristotle's ideas about the nature of air and wind seem strange to us today, others have a quite modern ring. Yet Aristotle's theories could not have been of much practical value to the sailors whose lives depended on the winds and the farmers whose livelihood varied with the rains. From observation and necessity, farmers and sailors developed their own weather wisdom.

Among men of learning, Aristotle's ideas about the atmosphere held sway unchallenged for more than a thousand years. In Roman times, however, and throughout the Middle Ages, a large body of weather lore developed among the people. Guided by this proverbial wisdom, handed down from one generation to the next or cellected by writers like Virgil, every man was his own weather expert. The flights of birds, the behavior of insects, the creakings of furniture—almost every imaginable phenomenon on earth and in the skies, it seemed!—had a bearing on the coming weather. Some of the proverbs relating weather to the appearance of the sky and the wind show keen powers of observation. Probably the average man, in spite of the large burden of superstition that he carried, was more weatherwise than the city-dweller of today, whose forecast comes ready-made from the experts. In short, although weather and climate were extremely important to people and their activities, so much so that the people developed their own folk meteorology, meteorology as a science cannot be said to have contributed much to society before the seventeenth century.

With the arrival of the Age of Discovery, the need for a better understanding of winds and weather became more pressing. Although a knowledge of weather has always been important for agriculture, it was then even more vital to commerce and to the world's navies. The voyages of the English buccaneer William Dampier and other mariners resulted in the first systematic compilation of the winds over the ocean, by Edmund Halley in 1688. It is probably fair to say that the establishment and growth of meteorological services have always resulted primarily from the needs of transport, whether of merchant shipping, navies, or, in recent times, commercial and military aviation. The first fully official national weather service was established in France in 1855, following the destruction of a French warship by a storm in the Black Sea the previous year and a study designed to avoid disasters of this kind.

The first official weather service in the United States began in the Army Signal Corps in 1870, primarily as an aid to shipping on the Great Lakes and along the Atlantic coast. The Weather Bureau, established under the Department of Agriculture in 1891, underwent a considerable expansion in the 1930's with the development of commercial aviation and its requirements for a specialized weather service. Finally, with the arrival of the Space Age, weather services were called on to supply data for the launching and re-entry of rockets and their payloads, and for weather conditions in landing areas.

In a modern society, however, not only transport but a host of other activities make meteorology a vital service. Population growth and settlement in marginal lands and along exposed beaches have made communities more vulnerable to droughts, tornadoes, hurricanes, and floods. The extraction of radioactive materials and the production of nuclear power produce dangerous wastes that must be released only under atmospheric conditions that insure their safe dispersal. Industries and automobiles produce airborne materials that accumulate under adverse weather conditions, resulting in illness and many deaths among thousands of persons. Warnings of these potentially dangerous conditions have become part of the forecaster's stock-in-trade, and he issues these routinely, just as he warns of severe thunderstorms and tornadoes, hurricanes with their high winds and capacity for flooding coastal areas, and blizzards that might otherwise take the lives of unwary motorists or kill entire herds of cattle.

Modern methods of agriculture, concerned with high volumes of food production per acre, require specialized forecasting services for spraying operations, planting, harvesting, irrigation, and protection against cold waves. The setting of forest fires by lightning and careless campers is closely related to weather conditions, so another specialized service is concerned with fire weather. Gas and power companies require forecasts in order to anticipate unusual demands on fuel and power, while power and telephone companies have to be aware of expected damage to lines from winds, lightning, and ice storms. City governments must have snow warnings to prepare for snow removal from the streets, and the commuter must know when it would be foolhardy to take his car out.

It appears, then, that our complex society requires more and more specialized services as new technologies develop. Meteorological services are, indeed, an integral part of any modern society, so much so that many vital activities could not be carried on safely and efficiently without them.

Like the other environmental sciences, meteorology requires cooperation among nations to an unusual degree. The atmosphere does not recognize any national boundaries. Because weather systems travel, forecasters have to look beyond their own areas of responsibility to anticipate the movement of storms into these areas. However, weather changes result not only from the motion of disturbances, but also from changes that are related to other changes perhaps thousands of miles away. To produce reliable forecasts two to three days in advance, meteorologists need observations over a large part of the hemisphere. Moreover, airlines flying to other countries need up-to-the-minute forecasts along their extensive routes and at airports where the planes land. Almost as soon as national weather services came into being, requirements for the exchange and standardization of observations and codes led to international committees, and from these developed an International Meteorological Organization. The successor to this body, the World Meteorological Organization, is an agency of the United Nations that directs the coordination of matters common to the national weather services. Indeed, meteorology has proved to be an important vehicle for cooperation among nations, and current plans for a World Weather Program are extending this cooperation.

HISTORY OF MODERN METEOROLOGY

ALTHOUGH MODERN METEOROLOGY may be said to have begun with the creation of the weather map by H. W. Brandes in 1820, its foundations were laid by many famous scientists, beginning with Galileo (1564-1642), who found the atmosphere a convenient laboratory. The basis of science is quantitative measurement, and Galileo contributed to meteorology the invention of the thermometer, while his pupil Torricelli, in demonstrating that the air has weight, incidentally discovered the principle of the barometer. The work of Galileo and Torricelli on atmospheric pressure was completed by Blaise Pascal, who by carrying a barometer up the Ppy-de-Dôme in France (1648) showed that the pressure of the atmosphere decreases with increasing altitude.

With the construction of barometers, it soon became evident that the atmospheric pressure varies also with changing weather conditions, and observations soon became the basis for using the "weather glass," as the barometer was called, as a forecasting instrument. In the nineteenth century, Fitzroy of the British Admiralty developed a mercury barometer suitable for use at sea, and made a list of instructions for interpreting its changes in terms of changes of wind and weather. Although there is a physical basis for many of these rules, the barometer used alone, or even in conjunction with the thermometer following Admiral Fitzroy's practice, is a very crude forecasting tool.

However, simultaneous barometirc readings collected from a network of observing stations, when plotted, form the basis for the weather map. The reign of the weather map began after the invention of the telegraph in 1835, when it became possible to collect the observations of pressure and other weather elements quickly enough to use the data for current forecasting. The relationship between wind and pressure, which earlier meteorologists had suspected, became more obvious when the observations were plotted on maps. In 1857, the Dutch meteorologist Buys-Ballot formulated his famous rule, which states that if an observer in the Northern Hemisphere stands with his back to the wind, low pressure is to his left and high pressure to his right. The relation between wind and pressure distribution is caused essentially by the rotation of the Earth on its axis, as the Frenchman Coriolis demonstrated mathematically in the early 19th century.

The weather map quickly became the basis for practical forecasting and led to the establishment of meteorological services in the United States and in the countries of western Europe. Observation stations were set up, their reports collected and plotted, and the forecaster's job became one of anticipating the changes in the pressure patterns on his map. These patterns, at the Earth's surface, form areas of high and low pressure that, in middle latitudes, usually move in an overall west-to-east direction, with their accompanying weather.

There is a limit to the skill one can achieve in forecasting simply by observing the changes in weather patterns at the Earth's surface. The use of kites and balloons to carry recording instruments high into the atmosphere marked another advance in meteorology. These early upper-air observations resulted in one of the most unexpected discoveries in the history of the science. Meteorologists had long assumed that the temperature continued to decrease indefinitely above the Earth's surface, but in 1899-1902 Teisserence de Bort, using data from a great many such *soundings* of the atmosphere, showed that above the layer of decreasing temperature is a layer in which the temperature remains constant, or increases, with altitude. He named the lower region the *troposphere*, which means "sphere of mixing," and he called the region above the *stratosphere,* to indicate its stratified or homogenous condition. Most of the atmosphere's weather, as we know it, occurs in the troposphere.

During World War I, meteorographs—the instruments carried into the atmosphere to record the temperature, pressure, and humidity—contributed to the greatest advance in the science up to that time, since the invention of the weather map. Cut off from weather reports from the rest of the world, a group of Norwegian meteorologists led by Vilhelm Bjerknes and his son, Jacob, established a close network of observing stations in Norway and began to develop a new method of analysis that included not only surface weather but the entire mass of air above, at least to the extent that it could be observed directly or by interpretation of cloud forms. Bjerknes's group thus developed the theory and practice of *air mass and frontal analysis.* They concluded from their studies that air masses of different origin (for example, from the tropics and from polar regions) maintain their characteristic properties of temperature and moisture, and are separated from each other by *frontal surfaces.* A *front* appears where the frontal surface intersects the Earth's surface, and was so named, by analogy with the military "fronts," because this region is a kind of battleground between the opposing forces of warm and cold air.

The Norwegian group also developed a theory explaining the origin of cyclones along frontal surfaces and the processes that take place during the growth and final decay of a cyclone. The polar front theory was marked by extensive use of physical theory to account for weather and its changes. The three-dimensional approach, in contrast to the two-dimensional view of the conventional surface weather map, as well as the close application of physical principles, made the frontal theory a much more powerful tool for weather analysis and forecasting.

Bjerknes was a physicist, and his ultimate aim was to apply the equations of physics to the atmosphere in such a rigorous fashion that forecasts could be made on a sound scientific basis. Unfortunately, he did not achieve that goal, for the system developed by his group was still an individual, nonquantitative method of analysis and forecasting. Even while the Norwegian group was perfecting its method, however, an English meteorologist named Lewis F. Richardson was pushing Bjerknes's aim a step forward. Richardson's scheme was ambitious. It was nothing less than to substitute into the equations of motion, and the other equations describing the atmosphere, the observed meteorological quantities and to predict their changes in short steps by numerical integration of the equations.

Numerical integration, as its name implies, is simply a way of solving equations by an arithmetical, as opposed to an analytical, method. Richardson's concept was simple, but very laborious to carry out. It is based on the fact that the equations describing atmospheric processes involve the *time* change of certain quantities in relation to the *spatial* distribution of other quantities. Thus, if one knows the distribution of pressure, temperature, and other elements on a weather map, it is possible, in principle, to compute the corresponding change of the quantities at that particular time. By assuming that this computed change will approximate the change taking place during the next few minutes, it is then possible to find the distribution of all the quantities a short time later. Then the change corresponding to the forecast distribution is computed, in order to obtain a new distribution at still another time in the near future. This process is repeated until a forecast for the desired time is obtained. However, for a forecast involving a sizeable area a day or so in advance, many, many thousands of computations are required, even when the equations have been highly simplified by leaving out presumably unimportant terms.

Richardson, a Quaker, was a medical corpsman during World War I, and while he was on duty in France, he carried out the computations, laboriously by hand, for his experiment in numerical weather prediction. The story goes that his manuscript was lost in a coal bin and only recovered many months later. Although his experiment did not give realistic values for the predicted pressure changes and was in that sense a failure, it did set an example for future meteorologists to follow and improve upon. The next such experiment, however, was not to come until after World War II. Perhaps meteorologists were deterred by Richardson's estimate that it would take some 6,000 clerks, working steadily, to carry out the computations in time to make a useful forecast!

Between the wars, and during War II, a number of important advances were made in meteorological instruments and theory. The *radiosonde* made it possible to send instruments to ·greater heights and to obtain measurements which were transmitted back to the ground stations immediately. One of the Bjerknes assistants, Carl-Gustaf Rossby, came to the United States, where he developed a theory of upper-air motions that was to be used in later numerical experiments. The development of airplane weather reconnaissance and of radar, during World

War II, made it possible to spot and investigate hurricanes and severe local storms. After the war, meteorological rockets brought new knowledge about the very high atmosphere.

Finally, in 1948, on one of the first of the newly developed electronic computers, a group working at Princeton University, under the leadership of the Hungarian mathematician John von Neumann, carried out the first successful experiment in numerical weather prediction. Although working forecasters were at first skeptical of the ultimate worth of the numerical method, developments during the following twenty years placed it on a sound footing. Forecasters now take the machine-made forecast as a best first estimate, modify it where they think necessary, and turn out a better forecast than they could have made without the aid of the computer. Numerical prediction has also extended the period over which useful forecasts can be made.

On April 1, 1960, the launching of the first weather satellite TIROS 1 (for Television Infrared Observation Satellite), marked still another advance for meteorology. The latest satellites reveal the entire Earth's cloud cover, permitting meteorologists to analyze their weather maps more accurately in places where there are few other weather observations and to detect hurricanes and other storms over vast, little-traveled areas of the oceans. A number of ground stations over the world are able to receive photographs of clouds over a wide area around the station, and these are of great value in making local forecasts and in briefing pilots. However, as useful as these observations are, it is the satellite's potentiality that intrigues meteorologists. In 1969, an important breakthrough came when radiation data from Nimbus 3 made it possible to determine the detailed temperature distribution in the atmosphere where the sky is not obscured by clouds. Satellites may soon become the key elements in a world-wide network of weather observations.

THE OCEAN OF AIR

ALTHOUGH WE HAVE TALKED about meteorology at some length, we have said very little about the atmosphere itself, the object of the meteorologist's study. Indeed, this is not the place for more than the following brief account needed to acquaint you with the nature of the problems that future meteorologists will be trying to solve. You will find references for further study in the Bibliography, page 177.

The atmosphere is a mixture of gases, the so-called permanent or nonvarying gases like nitrogen, oxygen, carbon dioxide, and argon, and variable gases like water vapor, ozone, and a number of trace gases. Like water, air is a fluid, a substance that is not rigid like a solid but is free to flow. The force that causes air to flow is the pressure produced by the weight of the atmosphere above—that is, by the action of gravity. Air tends to move from high to low pressure, but the Earth's rotation causes an apparent acceleration (to the right of the air's path in the Northern Hemisphere, to the left in the Southern Hemisphere) that results in a flow at right angles to the direction from high tol ow pressure. Thus the air tends to flow parallel to the isobars, the lines connecting equal pressure values on a weather map.

If you have studied physics, you know that weight is a result of the action of gravity on a particular mass. Different materials of the same volume weigh more or less because their densities are different. (Density is mass per unit volume.) Thus, if you consider the areas of high and low pressure at the Earth's surface, since the volumes of atmosphere above are the same, you can conclude that the average density over the high pressure center is greater than over the low center. There is more air over the high than over the low.

Since the density of a gas, moreover, is related to its temperature, it is essentially the different temperature of different parts of the atmosphere that produces the winds. Air tends to expand upward over warm regions, where it flows at upper levels toward cooler, denser portions of the atmosphere, just as water runs downhill. The addition of this air over the cooler regions causes the pressure to rise at the Earth's surface, so that the cold air is forced to move along the Earth's surface toward the warmer region from which some of the air had been exhausted. In this way a *circulation* is established.

The primary circulation of the atmosphere is caused by the heating of the air at low latitudes and the cooling at higher latitudes, resulting from the greater amount of solar enegery received closer to the equator. Air flowing poleward curves toward the east, and air flowing equatorward curves toward the west as a result of the Earth's rotation. At middle and high latitudes, where warm and cold air are brought close together, the polar front is formed, and cyclones and anticyclones develop along this front. These cyclones and anticyclones usually travel in the direction of the westerly winds aloft. In the tropics, cyclones are formed in quite a different way, there being little difference between air masses that travel toward the west until they recurve into the region of the westerlies.

Weather is caused primarily by the air's motion and the change of state of water vapor, which, in turn, are related to the motion. When air rises, it cools because it expands against the lower pressure at high elevations. When water vapor reaches a certain temperature—called the dew-point temperature—it becomes *saturated,* and at this point condenses on tiny solid particles (condensation nuclei), forming clouds. Although clouds and rain can be caused by cooling from other processes, it is upward motion that is primarily responsible for condensation in the atmosphere. Similarly, downward motion produces warming and lower relative humidity.

THE AIMS OF METEOROLOGY

THE METEOROLOGIST'S main scientific task is this: given the size, shape, topography, and motions of the Earth, the energy output of the sun, and the composition of dry air, to predict the observed motions and other processes going on in the atmosphere. Only in recent years, with the aid of the computer, have meteorologists been able to start with such "first principles" and to predict what happens as the atmosphere heats up at the equator, as water evaporates into the atmosphere from the oceans, storms develop, and precipitation occurs.

Since the meteorologist must determine how much heat and water are transferred from the Earth's surface to the air, he is interested in the distribution of land and water and in the amounts of energy these bodies contain. He is interested in the composition of the air, how it absorbs and transmits energy received from the sun and from the Earth's surface, so that he can compute the *radiative* temperature changes that occur, as well as those that are caused by the bodily transport of air masses. He needs to know how the Earth's surface and how clouds *reflect* solar radiation, which is thus lost to the Earth without influencing the atmosphere. He needs to understand the *dynamics* of motion systems on many scales, from the general circulation of the entire atmosphere, to monsoons, hurricanes, sea breezes, thunderstorms, and tornadoes, down to the small eddies called *turbulence*. And he must learn about the ways in which cloud droplets form on tiny nuclei in the air, and how these droplets unite to form a raindrop (It takes about one million cloud droplets to make a drop of rain!) either in the presence of ice crystals or through the coalescence of cloud droplets.

This is only a sketchy outline of some of the main problems that the meteorologist must solve in order to be able to predict the weather accurately. In addition to forecasting weather, he hopes to be able eventually to explain why the climate of the Earth has undergone such great changes during geological time, from ice ages to periods much milder than our own, and to predict future climatic changes. Many explanations have been advanced for these alterations of climate: variations in the sun's energy output; long-period changes in the position of the Earth relative to the sun; changes in volcanic activity and the atmospheric dust content due to volcanic eruptions; changes in the carbon dioxide content of the atmosphere; and changes in the distribution and elevation of the land due to the drifting of the continents, mountain building, and the eroding of the land— to name only the most important.

Increased fuel consumption since the start of the industrial revolution has caused an increase in the atmosphere's carbon dioxide, and calculations show that this increase might have accounted in part for the warming that took place over much of the world from the nineteenth century to about 1940. There is evidence, however, that since the mid-1940s the temperature of the Earth has declined slightly, in spite of the continued output of carbon dioxide. Meteorologists have speculated that part of the cooling may be due to an increase in industrial dusts in the atmosphere as well as to greater volcanic activity, but the possible effect of pollution on the world's climate is not yet resolved.

However, marked changes in the local and, in some cases, the regional climates of the world have been observed to be related to urban development and industrial activity. One can watch the condensation trails left by jet aircraft and watch them merge into a layer of high cloud. How much of the world's high cloudiness along jet routes is now the result of these *contrails* and what, if any, is their effect on other aspects of climate? These are the kinds of questions that meteorologists are being called on to solve.

Recently, too, meteorologists have begun to inquire seriously into various suggestions that large-scale changes in climate might be brought about intentionally—that weather and climate might be made to order. Indeed, weather modification operations to induce rain and suppress hail have been going on now for some years, in addition to experiments to determine to what extent these operations are successful. There is considerable evidence that, under the proper conditions of clouds and moisture supply, Dry Ice or silver iodide dropped into clouds (cloud seeding) can often cause the clouds to yield more precipitation than they would naturally. Experiments with tropical cumulus clouds and those clouds caused by the movement of air over mountains have been particularly successful. Meteorologists are even cautiously optimistic over the possibility of eventually modifying hurricanes. Fogs are being dispersed from military airports by seeding to permit additional planes to land and take off, and fog dispersal is also being tried at commercial airports.

Before the advent of the computer, such problems as long-range weather prediction and the assessment of schemes for modifying the world's climate seemed almost too formidable to be taken seriously. The problems themselves were too large and complex; only piecemeal solutions seemed possible. One of the main difficulties that faced meteorologists was the problem of *feedback,* or secondary changes. Suppose, for example, that one could produce cloud and rain over a large area. What effect would the presence of the cloud layer have on future changes? The area would certainly receive less solar radiation, for much of the sun's energy would be reflected back to space from the tops of clouds. How would this affect the general circulation? Would one end by decreasing instead of increasing the rainfall, as intended? The advantage of the systematic, quantitative approach to such problems, made possible by the computer, is that fewer such threads of cause and effect are left dangling; they are included in the calculations. In this sense, the computer can "think" a problem through more successfully than can the scientists who tell it how and what to "think."

Of course, there are both theoretical and practical limitations to what can be done. The meteorologist is sometimes forced to treat certain "variable constants" as constant. The model that he has constructed may be so complex that the machine is unable to arrive at a solution within a reasonable length of time. But the fact that research groups have been able to start with the atmosphere at rest, supply the appropriate amounts of solar energy, and in this way produce weather maps that still bear a resemblance to actual weather patterns after one hundred "days," is a strong indication that progress is being made in such experiments. In another experiment, precipitation areas were correctly forecast many days ahead, from observed data put into the equations, even though the weather systems causing the precipitation were not present on the initial map. In still another experiment, the world's climates have been reproduced from the distribution of land and water and solar energy.

THE FUTURE OF METEOROLOGY

IF, IN METEOROLOGY, one looked for the kind of accuracy that astronomers attain in predicting the path of an eclipse, meteorologists would have little grounds for optimism in looking to the future of their science. Very probably, it will never be possible to predict the exact time of beginning and ending of rain, or the exact time and place of a thunderstorm or tornado, at any appreciable time in advance. There will always be an element of uncertainty in the weather forecast, if for no other reason than that the scale of many disturbances is so small that it would be economically unfeasible to make the measurements required to predict them. Meteorologists have been most successful in observing and predicting the larger-scale disturbances that affect broad areas and that indicate, in a statistical sense, where the smaller-scale showers, thunderstorms, and tornadoes are likely to occur. In addition to improving these forecast of a few hours to two or three days, it seems likely that the greatest advances in the coming decades will be made in long-range forecasting and perhaps in weather and climate control.

For the past few years, meteorologists have been planning a World Weather Program, an outgrowth of a resolution on the peaceful uses of outer space presented to the United Nations Assembly by President John F. Kennedy. This international program has two objectives. One of the aims is to improve the world's observational network, weather communications systems, and organization of forecasting, so that all of the nations of the world will be supplied with adequate warnings and forecasts. The operational weather satellites of the United States have already made it possible to move toward this goal by supplying cloud photographs to countries that are able to install relatively inexpensive ground equipment to receive the pictures. Particularly in countries affected by tropical cyclones, the satellite pictures have provided warnings where none, or almost none, were available before. The plans for the World Weather Program go farther, however, than the use of current techniques.

One that has already been tested is to release a large number of balloons that float with the wind at the same level, day after day. Some of these balloons will carry instruments to measure temperature, pressure, and humidity, and will be located and interrogated by satellite to determine wind velocity and the other elements. Buoys are being designed to be anchored at regular intervals in the oceans, in order to increase the number of surface reports. Finally, it has been shown recently (1969) that satellites are able to sound the atmosphere directly to obtain the vertical distribution of temperature: the quantity currently most adaptable for use in numerical weather prediction. Satellite measurements are thus an important part of the plan.

The other aim of the overall plan is to obtain sufficient measurements over the world to experiment with a complex mathematical model of the atmosphere. This part of the plan, called the Global Atmosphere Research Program, will be developed during the 1970s. One of the present difficulties in numerical experiments is that the areas of incomplete data so affect the forecasts that the results are uncertain; another is that the observations are not adequate to test the results accurately.

Preliminary studies have indicated that useful forecasts up to about two weeks in advance will be possible when the atmosphere is adequately observed. The economic benefits to the world from such long-range forecasts will be enormous, and the opportunities for meteorologists supplying information to industry, agriculture, and commerce will be many times greater than they are now. Just as many large businesses today employ economists to predict trends in production and markets, so in the future it is likely that most will find a great economic advantage in having meteorologists on their staffs. Agriculture, food processing, shipping and trucking industries, utilities, chain stores, and construction are some of the activities that will stand to reap great benefits from more accurate estimates of the coming weather. In the world of business, "perfect" forecasts are not necessary to show a profit from the correct use of weather predictions that are correct part of the time. One study, for example, has shown that, even at present forecast accuracy, it would be possible for the construction industry, using modern decision-making theory based on cost-loss considerations, to save between one-half and one billion dollars annually in the United States.

A famous scientist, Irving Langmuir, once remarked that it might be easier to control the weather than to forecast it. However, without accurate predictions, one's claim to cotnrol of the weather would necessarily be in doubt, and meteorologists have usually held that improved prediction should logically be the first goal. It would then be possible, using numerical techniques, to make such alterations as the modifying experiment would produce, and rerun the forecast in order to observe the effects of the modification. This, in essence, is the plan that some researchers have for carrying out "experimental" weather modification projects, as opposed to actual projects. The Defense Department and the National Oceanic and Atmospheric Administration, in planning hurricane modification experiments, have been careful to restrict their operations to storms that are unlikely to affect any land area. Related experiments on cumulus clouds have been carefully planned and controlled, and actual measurements of seeded and unseeded clouds in the vicinity have been used, in conjunction with the theory of cumulus development, to interpret the results.

Obviously, if control of weather and climate on a large scale should prove to be physically and economically feasible, meteorology would acquire a novel position among the sciences. No less a scientist than John von Neumann once prophesied that within the lifetime of young people today, man will be in control of his climate on a scale difficult to imagine now. Carl-Gustaf Rossby, commenting on this prophecy, said, "One should remember that during the last decades technological development has time after time shown the dreams of a visionary mind to be closer to reality than the common sense judgment of the realist."

Even discounting such bold glimpses into the future, there is ample evidence that meteorology today is on the threshold of new and perhaps revolutionary advances. The challenges of the atmosphere no longer seem insurmountable, and meteorology's opportunity to contribute to the general welfare is rapidly expanding. The coming decades will be exciting ones for the young scientist of today who elects meteorology as his field.

CHAPTER 3

PLANNING A METEOROLOGICAL EDUCATION

CAREER GOALS, intellectual capabilities, and financial resources all enter into planning an education. These factors, of course, differ widely among individuals. Fortunately for the student who elects meteorology as a career, the curricula at American universities are quite varied and meet many differing requirements, and tuition costs show a wide range.

While the requirements for a professional degree in older fields may be fairly rigid, the student of meteorology has a variety of choices. We have already pointed out that some universities treat meteorology as a graduate study exclusively; these schools offer graduate degrees in meteorology, but not undergraduate degrees. Others have undergraduate departments offering the bachelor's degree in meteorology or atmospheric science, making it possible for the student in a four-year course to gain familiarity with the fundamental concepts of meteorology and its practice in preparation for professional work. The student may then either get a job or continue studying; most of these schools offer graduate as well as undergraduate degrees in the field. Still other institutions, though few in number, offer only an undergraduate curriculum in meteorology. The following statistics illustrate this diversity.

During the 1969-70 academic year, there were 58 colleges and universities in the United States with curricula in the atmospheric sciences [1]. Of these, seven offered only the bachelor's degree; 20 offered only graduate degrees (M.S. and Ph.D.); and 31 offered both undergraduate and graduate degrees.

These figures indicate that the educational standards for professional work in meteorology are far from rigid. For professional workers in meteorological operations and services, an undergraduate degree is usually regarded as sufficient, while for research meteorologists and university teachers, graduate study is essential. However, with the increasing application of scientific method to meteorology, a good case can be made for regarding some graduate study as highly desirable for professional work in most fields of meteorology.

EDUCATIONAL REQUIREMENTS FOR METEOROLOGISTS

THE EDUCATIONAL REQUIREMENTS for meteorologists in the United States have been well summarized by Dr. Werner A. Baum, educator and former Deputy Administrator of ESSA, the predecessor to the recently organized National Oceanic and Atmospheric Administration [2]:

> Meteorology in the United States may be loosely divided into two categories: *service meteorology* and *research meteorology*. The former includes applications and most industrial activity; the latter includes development and university teaching. Obviously the groupings are general and subject to exceptions; but they are useful for the purpose at hand.

In service meteorology, most persons are employed in general and aviation forecasting. This branch of meteorology is of great importance and should be of major concern with regard to educational requirements. With the routine facsimile communication of computer-produced charts, including prognostic charts, to the forecasters in the secondary centers away from our World Weather Center, we note a curious development. Perhaps we should have foreseen it. We find that the more we supply the forecaster with predigested information, the more sophisticated must be his knowledge to use and interpret this information to make useful weather forecasts in the mesoscale. We find that he must know the theoretical concepts and mathematical pecularities which go into whatever numerical model is currently being used. To have a really intelligent understanding of these dynamical forecasting models, he needs quite a good education in fundamental physics, mathematics, and meteorology. This must be sound academic knowledge and not a cookbook or trade-school variety, because new dynamical models are continually evolving, requiring breadth of knowledge.

For this reason, the meteorologist whom the WMO (World Meteorological Organization) designates as Class II, and whom we term technicians rather than professionals (Class II), are becoming obsolete as forecasters in the United States. They cannot keep up with technological advances because of lack of academic scientific education, and retraining cannot keep up with their needs.

The university system in the United States offers all interested and qualified high school graduates opportunities to become Class I service meteorologists through the bachelor's program. The advantage of this system is that the young person does not have to commit himself to a choice between becoming a Class I or Class II meteorolo-

gist before he is sure of his potentialities. Nor does he
need to commit himself irrevocably to service or research
work at the outset of his education. He may freely develop
as his ability and motivation lead him. These are among
the advantages of having diversity of progressive (not
alternative) degree levels available rather than graduate
degrees only.

Aside from general and aviation weather forecasting,
other specializations in service meteorology might be
agricultural or marine meteorology. Each of these requires
additional education. Here again we depend upon the
universities, benefiting from the diversity at different
institutions which our economy is able to sustain.

The other main category with which we are concerned,
in government as well as in the universities and industry,
is research meteorology. A large variety of special fields is
encompassed here. Again, the fortunate diversity of specialized emphasis among our universities supplies ample
scope for the preparation of research workers. Thus, the
graduate student may select the university which empha-
sizes his major field of interest. Obviously the requirement
here is for Class I meteorologists with considerable
graduate-level education.

I have not included training, as distinct from education, in this presentation. It must not be overlooked
entirely. To me, training means the development of skills
which are specific to the duties to be performed. Let us
take weather forecasting as an example. Our universities
do not turn out finished, skilled forecasters; it is not their
intention to do so. They teach all the fundamental science
and mathematics incident to forecasting, and the concepts
needed for forecasting. The development of skills in specific techniques is largely the responsibility of the organization which hires the university graduates. Thus, training

of this kind is largely done outside the universities, either on the job or in special classes conducted by the hiring organization. But I must emphasize that the thorough education of the meteorologist must come first.

National and international requirements for education in meteorology were recently discussed in more detail at a symposium of the World Meteorological Organization [3].

OTHER GOALS AND METEOROLOGICAL CURRICULA

ALTHOUGH, AS POINTED OUT by Dr. Baum, the student who chooses meteorology as a career need not at the outset of his university work have mapped out the details of his education, he will nevertheless find it useful to have a general familiarity with the choices open to him. Some notion of the relation between careers and educational preparation is especially appropriate. For this reason, in Table 1 we have

TABLE 1

Subject Areas of Meteorology and Their Career Applications

Subject Areas	*Careers and Applications*
I. FUNDAMENTAL COURSES General meteorology, climatology, dynamic meteorology, physical meteorology, synoptic meteorology, meteorological instruments, statistical methods, forecasting	Service and operational careers Analysis and weather forecasting, weather station management and other operations, preparation for graduate study

Subject Areas

II. ATMOSPHERIC PHYSICS, CHEMISTRY, AND DYNAMICS
Atmospheric thermodynamics, dynamics of atmospheric motions, atmospheric chemistry, atmospheric electricity, atmospheric optics and accoustics, atmospheric composition, atmospheric radiation, cloud and precipitation physics, atmospheric turbulence and diffusion, micrometeorology

III. APPLIED METEOROLOGY
Weather analysis and forecasting, numerical analysis and prediction, mesometeorology, hydrometeorology, atmospheric pollution, satellite meteorology, meteorological observations, severe local storms, cyclones and anticyclones, hurricanes, tropical meteorology, polar meteorology, the stratosphere

IV. SERVICE AREA SPECIALIZATIONS
Air pollution meteorology, agricultural meteorology, fire-weather meteorology, marine meteorology, aviation meteorology

V. METEOROLOGICAL INSTRUMENTATION
Data sensing systems, balloon sounding systems, radar and radio instrumentation, rocket sounding systems, satellite instrumentation, radiation sensors, micrometeorological sensors

Careers and Applications

Research, university teaching, research management, and operational careers

Broad theoretical applications: general circulation research, causes of cloud and rain, remote sensing, climatic changes, weather modification, many other basic areas of careers

Service, operational, management, research and university teaching careers.

Analysis, forecasting, research; forecasting local storms, hurricanes, rivers and floods; interpretation of observations, design of networks, theory and forecasting of storms, forecasting air pollution potential

Service, operational, and applied research careers

Analysis, forecasting, and research

Research, operations, management, systems development, and university teaching careers

Design, development, test, and maintenance of instruments and instrument systems

Subject Areas	*Careers and Applications*
VI. CLIMATOLOGY Paleoclimatology, synoptic climatology, environmental health, bioclimatology, microclimatology, physical climatology, engineering climatology	Service, operational, research, and university teaching careers Research, agriculture, medicine, urban pollution, industrial applications
VII. RELATED DISCIPLINES Aeronomy, planetary atmospheres, solar physics, geomagnetism, oceanography, hydrology, geography, geology, geochemistry, seismology, volcanology	Research, management, university teaching, and secondary school teaching (Earth science) Ionospheric research, telecommunications, Earth-space research, air-sea interactions, water resources, engineering design, many environmental research applications

grouped the various subject areas of meteorology and closely related fields, and have related these in a very general way to careers. The subjects are also related to the types of research, operations, or services for which they prepare the student. The subject areas are not necessarily the names of courses offered at universities, for the latter differ widely among the various schools.

The subjects under Group I are those traditionally offered as preparation for the bachelor's degree in meteorology. Essentially, these courses represents the minimum required for a professional rating in service or operational work, and are typical of those schools offering the bachelor's as the terminal degree or as preparation for advanced, specialized study. Some of the schools that offer only graduate degrees in atmospheric science also offer these fundamental courses at an advanced level.

The subjects in Group II are essentially a continuation or subdivision of the more basic courses in Group I, dynamic and

Global weather patterns are an important consideration in forecasting North American weather. Map discussions are a "way of life" at the National Meteorological Center.
Courtesy of NOAA

physical meteorology. Usually offered at the graduate level, these subjects are concerned with the fundamental properties and processes of the atmosphere and are essential to basic research in one or more of the areas of specialization.

Group II subjects, which one may find offered either at the graduate or undergraduate level, depending on the school, are more closely related to the operational aspects of meteorology than are the fundamental courses of Group II. They are largely concerned with the analysis and interpretation of data, with applied research, and with techniques of forecasting. Essentially, they constitute the many specialties that have arisen in synoptic meteorology in response to the requirements of forecasting, the development of special observing techniques, and the exploration of hitherto unknown regions of the atmosphere.

Group IV comprises the major services areas of meteorology. With the exception of agricultural meteorology and air pollution meteorology, these courses are not generally offered as formal courses at universities.

The subjects in Group V are essentially engineering subjects concerned with the techniques of acquiring meteorological data. These naturally lead to careers in instrument design and development, or in the maintenance and management of instrument systems.

Group VI, climatology, has very broad applications in the fields of agriculture, medicine, public health, urban planning, industry, and commerce. The fields of climatology are essentially service oriented, supplying long-term requirements not met on a day-to-day basis by weather forecasting. Paleoclimatology, however, falls in the area of basic research. The other fields also offer opportunities for research and development.

Group VII includes the subjects and disciplines in the environmental sciences most closely related to meteorology. Although aeronomy is an atmospheric science, it has not traditionally been considered part of the basic meteorological curriculum—perhaps because its applications are not concerned directly with the weather as we experience it but with phenomena in the high atmosphere. However, telecommunications and space travel have recently emphasized the practical aspects of aeronomy. Oceanography, on the other hand, traditionally has had close ties with meteorology because of the strong interaction between the lower atmosphere and the sea; interdisciplinary education and research in the two disciplines are long established. The study of the atmospheres of other planets has applications to the study of the Earth's atmosphere.

The trend toward specialization in meteorology has been accompanied by an almost equally marked trend toward treating the geophysical disciplines as a single science. Consequently, interdisciplinary education is assuming increased importance. At a number of universities, meteorology is now a part of a college or department of geosciences. The many diverse applications of meteorology and a renewed awareness of environmental problems have led to the organization of multidisciplinary programs at many universities. In government, the trend toward unification of the geophysical sciences was marked in 1970 by creation of the National Oceanic and Atmospheric Administration.

With some risk of oversimplification, one might summarize the relation between subject areas and careers in the following way: minimum requirement for service and operational careers, Group I; desirable for operation careers, Groups III and IV; desirable for service careers, Groups III, IV, and VI; careers in applied research, Groups III and VI; careers in basic research, Groups II and VII.

The colleges and universities in the United States and Canada that had curricula in the atmospheric sciences in 1970 are listed on pages 179-182. The list has been broken down into three groups: those offering both undergraduate and graduate degrees; those awarding undergraduate degrees only; and those offering only graduate degrees. The latter tend to emphasize theoretical rather than applied or operational aspects of meteorology. In many cases they concentrate exclusively on specialized areas of investigation (e.g., cloud and precipitation physics, aeronomy, planetary atmospheres, or biometeorology), and prepare the student primarily for careers in research or university teaching. Universities offering only the undergraduate degree in meterology, on the other hand, emphasize the applied and practical aspects of meteorology in order to prepare the student for an operational or service career. About two-thirds of the schools offering both undergraduate and graduate work provide training in the more traditional, fundamental aspects of meteorology, so that the student has a choice between preparing for research, teaching, or an operational and service career.

Because the curricula in atmospheric science at the various universities differ quite widely, the student should consult university catalogs for more specific details. Comparisons between the course offerings at the different schools can be made readily by consulting the latest edition of *Curricula in the Atmospheric Sciences* [1]. Many meteorology programs or departments are fairly small and highly specialized. Some, for example, prepare the student primarily for a career in education (teaching Earth science in the high schools), in climatology, in cloud and precipitation physics, in air pollution meteorology, or in some other specialized area. To be sure of matching his education to his interests and goals, the student should choose a college only after careful study of the available curricula.

UNDERGRADUATE STUDY

ALTHOUGH THERE ARE VARIATIONS in the meteorology curricula of universities offering the bachelor's degree, in general, about 40 percent of the studies are in mathematics and the physical sciences; about 30 percent are in the humanities and social sciences; and about 30 percent are in meteorology. A fairly typical curriculum would be as follows:

	Semester Hours		*Semester Hours*
Freshman Year		*Junior Year*	
English	6	Mathematics	9
Chemistry	6	Physics	9
Mathematics	9	Meteorology	4
Meteorology	3	History	6
General Education (Electives)	6	General Education (Electives)	4
Physical Education	2	Total	32
Total	32		
Sophomore Year		*Senior Year*	
English	6	Meteorology	30
Physics	10	Elective	2
Mathematics	6	Total	32
Meteorology	4		
General Education (Electives)	6		
Total	32		

In the first two or three years, the student concentrates on the traditional liberal arts and sciences, with, however, emphasis on mathematics and the basic physical sciences. Courses in meteorology or related Earth sciences may be taken during the first two years for familiarization purposes, or may be deferred until the junior year when, ordinarily, the student is expected to choose a major. Thus it would be readily possible for a student to complete the freshman and sophomore years at a junior college or other four-year liberal arts college or university not offering meteorology, and then transfer to one of the schools having a curriculum in atmospheric science. In either case, he should attempt to complete the basic courses in mathematics and the physical sciences that are prerequisite to the study of meteorology. These normally include mathematics through calculus, chemistry, and the standard physics courses (with laboratory) covering mechanics, heat and thermodynamics, optics, and electricity and magnetism.

If the student has definitely decided on a career in basic research or university teaching, he might consider deferring the study of meteorology until graduate school. In this case, he should substitute mathematics, the basic physical sciences, and perhaps some of the other geosciences for meteorology, taking a B.A. or B.S. in one of these areas. He should also consider the study of a foreign language in order to prepare for the language exams usual in many graduate schools. If he plans an interdisciplinary career, combining meteorology with biology, agronomy, oceanography, electrical engineering, or environmental engineering, for example, he might take his undergraduate degree in one of these fields. The schools that offer only the graduate degree in meteorology or atmospheric science usually prefer students well qualified in mathematics and the basic physical sciences.

Even if the student has decided on an operational or service career, he would do well to consider continuing with graduate study after taking his undergraduate degree, provided he is qualified. With the ever-increasing application of the science to meteorological operations and services, the distinction between operations and research tends to become blurred in many tasks, and the M.S. degree or its equivalent in graduate work is often regarded as a necessary qualification.

GRADUATE STUDY

AT THE GRADUATE LEVEL, most students begin to specialize, and graduate curricula are therefore more diversified than undergraduate courses. Most departments of meteorology require the student to prepare a thesis under the guidance of a member of the faculty. The choice and pursuit of a thesis naturally involve some expression and dedication of interest on the part of the student. His choice of a thesis may also have some bearing on his future assignment by his employer. Thus, by the time he enters graduate school, the student's interests should have crystallized to some extent so that he can choose the specialized courses in an area that most appeals to him. Some idea of the variety of fields among which he may choose is shown in Table 1. The choice ranges over fields as diverse as agricultural meteorology, telecommunications, and numerical analysis, and over areas of the atmosphere as remote from one another as the air-ocean interface and the ionosphere.

The requirements for the master's degree differ among the various institutions. The standard course requirement is 30 semester hours, which ordinarily must be taken in residence. Some universities require a reading knowledge of a foreign language; others do not. Some require the preparation of a thesis that must be approved by a committee of the faculty; others require only the completion of a certain number of courses, and sometimes the conclusion of a project assigned to the student.

Ordinarily, the course work can be completed in one academic year, and the thesis in another six months to a year.

Requirements for the doctorate in meteorology are naturally much more stringent than those for the master's degree. A dissertation is always required, in addition to approximately 30 semester hours of courses beyond those required for the master's degree. The dissertation must be based upon original research or creative scholarship. A reading knowledge of two foreign languages is usually required. The Ph.D. candidate must appear before a committee to be examined, orally, for his proficiency in the science. Ordinarily, about three years of graduate work are needed to complete the course and dissertation requirements for the doctorate. At most schools, students permitted to enroll as candidates for the doctoral degree have shown either exceptional performance in earlier academic work or, in the case of mature individuals who have some years of working experience, outstanding contributions in research or other areas of meteorology.

ENTRANCE REQUIREMENTS

THE COLLEGE ENTRANCE REQUIREMENTS of schools offering curricula in atmospheric science are much the same as those for other institutions: usually, graduation from high school with at least a B average in the required high school courses, and no grade below C in these courses. The subjects required are those ordinarily included in the "college preparatory" course —that is, English, a foreign language, mathematics, a laboratory science, and history. Usually, 10 to 12 or 16 to 18 units in these subjects, depending on whether three or four years of high school are taken as the base, are required. (A unit is a one-year course.) Most colleges or universities now require the College

Entrance Examination Board Scholastic Aptitude and Achievement Tests, or equivalent state Board of Regents tests. Some specify an "advanced" mathematics or science course in high school for the student to qualify for the college in which meteorology is offered. To be certain he meets the entrance requirements of the school to which he wishes to be admitted, the student should ask his guidance counselor about these requirements as early as the beginning of his junior year in high school.

Entrance requirements of graduate schools are similar to those for undergraduate schools: that is, at least a B average in the prerequisite undergraduate courses, with no grade below C in these courses, as well as the approval of the department head and the dean of the graduate school. Some schools require the applicant to have passed the Graduate Record Examinations with a satisfactory score.

COST OF EDUCATION AND FINANCIAL ASSISTANCE

SINCE EDUCATION COSTS are rising rapidly, the student should get figures on tuition costs and other fixed fees, as well as estimates of expenses for room and board, from the latest college or university catalog. In general, tuition and living expenses are lower at publicly supported colleges and universities than at privately supported schools. The following figures are an indication of how the two categories compare, as well as of how college costs are rising.

For state residents at state-supported schools in 1955-56, the *median* cost for one academic year was $838; in 1965-66 it was $979; and by 1975-76 it is expected to be $1,150. At privately supported schools, the median cost was $1,386 in 1955-56,

$1,982 in 1965-66, and by 1975-76 is expected to be $2,598. These are median figures for all schools, and it is probable that corresponding figures for schools offering meteorology are higher. For example, in 1967 the average cost at six state-supported universities offering meteorology, widely distributed over the country, was $1,314 for state residents and $1,822 for out-of-state residents. Costs at privately supported universities offering meteorology were considerably higher, and ranged as high as $3,600 per year. By 1971 the Bureau of Labor's cost-of-living index had risen about 20 percent over the 1967 value, and education costs were reflecting this rise.

One way for a student to reduce his total education costs is to take his "preprofessional" work at a local or community junior college, if his community provides one. Junior colleges offer the courses the student would be required to take, in any case, during his first two years of college; their tuition costs are usually much lower than regular four-year colleges; and living at home is less expensive than living out of town.

If the student or his family is unable to meet the heavy cost of a university education, he can often get financial assistance through loans, scholarships, grants, or, in some cases, part-time work. These financial assistance programs are, for the most part, administered by or through the institutions themselves; for detailed information the student should apply to the school he wishes to attend. Ordinarily, part-time laboratory, research, or teaching assistantships and fellowships are available to students at graduate schools having meteorology programs. Undergraduate students also are able to find employment at some schools. For example, at one of the state universities with a large meteorology department, in 1967, 25 of the 60 undergraduate students in their junior and senior years were employed by the department. Thirty-five of the 48 graduate students enrolled held fellowships and assistantships [4].

Since 1958, the federal government has assisted college students through loans and grants administered and, in part, supported by the schools. The National Defense Education Act of 1958 provided for a Student Loan Program, under which the federal government contributes 90 percent to the loan fund and the college ten percent. The undergraduate student, under this program, may borrow up to $1,000 per year; the total borrowed for undergraduate study may not exceed $5,000. Interest is 3 percent, and is deferred until nine months after the student finishes full- or part-time study, when he must begin to repay the loan. If the student goes into teaching, the loan itself may be cancelled at the rate of ten percent per year, up to a maximum of 50 percent of the amount borrowed. By 1967, under the National Student Loan Program, one million students had borrowed more than a billion dollars. Graduate students also are eligible to borrow under the program.

In addition, the Higher Education Act of 1965 instituted a Guaranteed Loan Program, under which students may obtain low-cost loans for education through banks and other loan companies. Here, the federal government pays the full interest on the loan during the student's college years, and three percent during repayment; the student pays the remaining portion of the interest charge on the unpaid balance. The same act established the Educational Opportunity Grant Program, under which outright grants may be made to students who have exceptional financial need and would not otherwise be able to attend college.

Most scholarships and grants are offered through or by the colleges and universities, and the student should apply directly to the institution. Others are offered by outside organizations. For additional information on financing college costs, the student may turn to his guidance counselor or to one of several books on the subject [5].

For undergraduate students who plan to become meteorologists in the military services, the Reserve Officers Training Corps programs of the U.S. Air Force and the U.S. Navy may provide financial assistance and insure entry into the service. (See Chapter 5.) During certain periods, new officers come into the Air Weather Service only from the Air Force Reserve Officers Training Corps.

EDUCATIONAL OPPORTUNITIES AFTER EMPLOYMENT

FOR THE METEOROLOGY STUDENT who must find a job before he has completed his education, there are many opportunities to continue taking formal courses. There are also opportunities to participate in various training programs if he works for one of the large agencies or is a member of the Armed Forces. Actually, one's education is never "completed" in our modern world, especially in a continually developing and changing field such as meteorology.

Obviously, the best opportunities for continuing graduate education while employed exist at universities. Here, the meteorologist can simultaneously teach or do research, pursue his formal courses, and work on a thesis, so that the difference between work and study may be hardly perceptible. Opportunities, particularly for graduate education, exist also in government employment and in the military services. Because two-thirds of all employed meteorologists are in the federal government's civilian and military services, the government has a strong interest in stimulating and supporting meteorological education. For example, the National Science Foundation supports programs of teacher preparation in the Earth sciences at summer institutes and at in-service institutes. Fellowship and traineeship opportunities for competent graduate students exist through programs funded by the National Science Foundation and the National Aeronautics and Space Administration. These programs provide stipends for living costs in addition to tuition and fees. The National Science Foundation has advanced fellowship programs at the postdoctoral, senior postdoctoral, and science faculty levels. For the student who has recently completed his formal education, the National Oceanic and Atmospheric Administration (NOAA) offers Postdoctoral Resident Research Associateships in meteorology, with a substantial stipend.

The government also assigns qualified personnel to universities for study in meteorology at full salary and at no cost to the student for tuition. The Air Force sends many of its officers to universities for both basic and advanced meteorological training. The Navy has its own Postgraduate School at Monterey, Calif., for training in meteorology and oceanography. During the academic year 1970-1971, the National Oceanic and Atmospheric Administration assigned 75 employees to universities for full-time training in meteorology and other disciplines. Forty-one percent of these employees were assigned to study meteorology, indicating the government's concern in meteorological education. In addition, selected employees of the National Weather Service were enrolled in full-time university studies in agricultural meteorology for one semester. Three four-week, full-time university courses in radar meteorology were scheduled periodically during the year, with 20 selected students enrolled in each course.

Under the Student Assistant Program, undergraduate students are given encouragement and financial support as summer employees in government. Many meteorology students take advantage of this opportunity, not only for the financial help but also to obtain practical experience and to learn about career possibilities. Summer employment is also available for high school students who are finalists in National Science Fair contests.

Since the primary justification of a military organization during peacetime is training for a national emergency, it is not surprising that the meteorological branches of the military services have strong educational and training programs. In order to have enough trained personnel to accomplish its mission, the Air Force's Air Weather Service requires about 230 weather officers (professional meteorologists) each year. Although meteorology graduates of the Air Force Reserve Officers Training Corps supply part of this requirement, by far the major part comes from the Air Weather Service's "basic" meteorology program. Although this program is primarily for officers, non-professionals also may qualify for training in meteorology under the Airman Education and Commissioning Program and be commissioned as weather officers. The basic meteorology program is from nine to 12 months long, and is essentially equivalent to the Group I curriculum shown in Table 1. In 1970, this basic program was conducted for the Air Weather Service by the following universities: New York University, Pennsylvania State University, San Jose State College, St. Louis University, Texas A & M University, North Carolina State University, the University of Oklahoma, the University of Texas, and the University of Utah. Minimum academic prerequisites for the course are completion of at least three years' college work with mathematics courses through integral calculus and six semester hours of physics with grades of C or better.

The Air Weather Service also enables weather officers to obtain graduate education in the atmospheric sciences and closely related sciences, and thus to earn a master's or even a doctor's degree, majoring in such diverse subjects as astronomy, mathematics, geophysics, computer science, operations research, astrophysics, or micrometeorology. All tuition is paid, and the officer receives his full pay and allowances during these assignments. In addition to most of the universities participating in the basic undergraduate program, the following universities also take part in the Air Weather Service's graduate program: Colorado State University, Florida State University, Massachusetts Institute of Technology, the University of Arizona, the University of California at Los Angeles, the University of Colorado, the University of Hawaii, the University of Washington, the University of Wisconsin, the University of Alaska, and the University of Michigan.

The majority of Navy and Marine Corps officers in the Naval Weather Service have received their training at the U.S. Naval Postgraduate School at Monterey, California (see Chapter 5). This school is fully accredited and offers both undergraduate and graduate programs. The General Meteorology Curriculum, a two-year program that may lead to a Bachelor of Science degree, prepares officers to become qualified meteorologists with some knowledge of oceanography and computer operations and techniques. The Advanced Meteorology Curriculum qualifies the student to conduct independent research and to earn the M.S. degree. Prerequisites for the latter curriculum are the B.S. degree and certain courses in mathematics and physics.

Thus it is quite possible and not unusual, especially for the individual who already has an undergraduate degree or several years of college work, to obtain his meteorological education after employment, with expenses paid. At many locations it is also possible for an employee to attend evening classes in meteorology, mathematics, or the physical sciences on a part-time basis; if he works for the government, the agency may pay tuition on courses more or less directly related to the employee's duties. Many meteorologists in the National Weather Service have obtained most of their formal college education in this way, often supplemented by a year's assignment at one of the universities. Past experience suggests that an individual qualified for academic work, who at the same time is sufficiently determined to get a meteorological education, usually manages to obtain it.

REFERENCES

1. American Meteorological Society. *Curricula in the Atmospheric Sciences, Academic Year* 1969-1970. Boston, Mass.: 1970.
2. Baum, Werner A. "Philosophy and Practice of Meteorological Education in the United States," *Bulletin of the American Meteorological Society,* Vol. 48, No. 10, October 1967.
3. World Meteorological Organization. *Proceedings of the WMO/-IAMAP Symposium on Higher Education and Training.* Secretariat of the World Meteorological Organization, Geneva: 1970. Unipub, Inc., P.O. Box 433, New York, N. Y. 10016.
4. American Meteorological Society. *Weatherwise,* Vol. 20, Nos. 3 & 5, June & October, 1967.
5. Splaver, Sarah. *Your College Education — How to Pay for It.* New York: Julian Messner, Division of Simon & Schuster, Inc., 1968.

CHAPTER 4

METEOROLOGY IN THE CIVIL SERVICE

ABOUT ONE-THIRD of the practicing meteorologists in the United States work in the civil service of the federal government. Although the Defense Department, the National Aeronautics and Space Administration, and several other federal agencies (Chapter 1) employ meteorologists, the great majority in civilian government work are employed by the National Oceanic and Atmospheric Administration (NOAA). NOAA includes a number of component organizations that were historically part of the U.S. Weather Bureau, the Coast and Geodetic Survey, and several other agencies involved in meteorology or oceanography. The governmental reorganization that created NOAA reflects both the interdisciplinary nature of environmental science and the economic advantages of using common facilities to observe and study the environment. In his Message to Congress proposing the establishment of both NOAA and the Environmental Protection Agency, July 9, 1970, President Nixon said, in part:

> As concern with the condition of our physical environment has intensified, it has become increasingly clear that

we need to know more about the total environment—land, water and air. . . .

The oceans and the atmosphere are interacting parts of the total environmental system upon which we depend not only for the quality of our lives, but for life itself.

We face immediate and compelling needs for better protection of life and property from natural hazards, and for a better understanding of the total environment—an understanding which will enable us more effectively to monitor and predict its actions, and ultimately, perhaps to exercise some degree of control over them.

The official statement of NOAA's mission indicates the breadth of its objectives:

NOAA will explore, map, and chart the global oceans, their geological cradles, their geophysical forces and fields, and their mineral and living resources. New physical and biological knowledge will be translated into systems capable of assessing the sea's potential yield, and into techniques which the nation and its industries can employ to manage, use, and conserve these animal and mineral resources.

NOAA will monitor and predict the characteristics of the physical environment — the exceedingly variable changes of atmosphere and ocean, sun and solid earth, gravity and geomagnetism—in real time, given sufficiently advanced knowledge and technology. It will warn against impending environmental hazards, and ease the human burden of hurricane, tornado, flood, tsunami, and other destructive natural events.

NOAA will monitor and predict such gradual and inexorable changes as those of climate, seismicity, marine-life distributions, earth tides, continental position, the planet's internal circulations, and the effects of human civilization and industry on the environment and oceanic life.

To accomplish these objectives, NOAA will draw upon the talent and experience of its personnel, the wide range of its facilities, and mutually important links between government, universities, and industry. NOAA and its institutional partners will develop the technology and the systems with which to comprehend this broad province of service and investigation—systems leading to effective resource assessment, utilization of environmental data, environmental monitoring and prediction, and, possibly, environmental modification and control. Here, the growing family of satellites, sensors, ships, data buoys, computers, and simulators, which have enriched scientific understanding and provided the base for essential environmental services in recent decades, will find their best achievement.

In these ways, NOAA will improve the safety and quality of life, the efficiency and timing of oceanic hunts and harvests, and man's comprehension, use, and preservation of his planetary home.

Obviously, meteorology is only one of the environmental disciplines of concern to NOAA; yet meteorology is well represented. Nearly every activity in which meteorologists are likely to be engaged, with the exception of formal teaching, is carried on in the agency. Thus, the typical work of career meteorologists can be fairly well understood by considering NOAA's meteorological activities in some detail, as we shall do in this chapter. The chapters following this one round out the picture of professional meteorology by describing the specialized work of meteorologists in the military services (Chapter 5); the requirements for teaching, research, and consulting careers

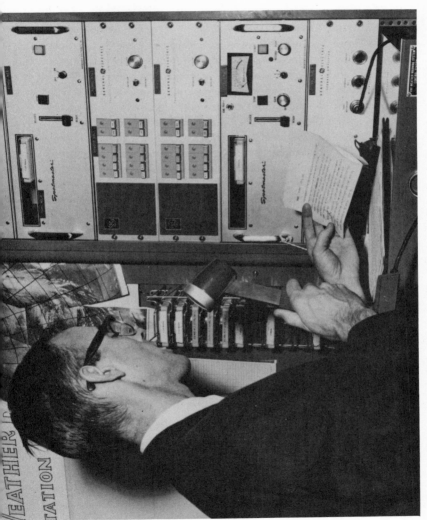

A fast warning system has long been the goal of weathermen. The recent intro-duction of NOAA VHF Radio Weather, now operational in more than 20 cities, approaches this goal.
Courtesy of NOAA

(Chapter 6); and meteorology in the "private sector," i.e., in business and industry (Chapter 7).

Typically, a national meteorological service has as its primary task to supply meteorological data, forecasts, and warnings to the country and also, through arrangements with the World Meteorological Organization, certain observations and services to the rest of the world. This task requires a network of observing and public service offices; a communications network; access to special observational facilities, like satellites, as well as other observing equipment; a forecasting system; a data center for archiving, processing, and publishing climatological data; a research program aimed at improving the services and the science on which the service vitally depends; and, usually, a documentation activity that includes library, information, and publishing services.

In NOAA, most of these functions are carried out in four of the major components of the agency: the National Weather Service, the Environmental Data Service, the National Environmental Satellite Service, and the Environmental Research Laboratories. The documentation activity is in the Environmental Data Service. These four components, together with NOAA headquarters, employ nearly all of the agency's meteorologists. About 5,000 of NOAA's employees are engaged in some phase of the work of weather forecasting and warning; 500 in climatological work; 450 in meteorological research; 400 in the environmental satellite service; and 350 in river and flood prediction and warning. The hydrologic work is closely integrated with the meteorological program, since river and flood predictions depend so closely on precipitation and on the melting of snow.

The work of these several thousand employees evolves naturally from NOAA's functions and programs. Certain broad categories of jobs and duties are self-evident. First of all, there must be *weather observers* to make the weather observations and report them. There must also be *weather forecasters* to predict the weather, and *briefers* and *public service meteorologists* to convey the forecasts and other weather information to those who use them. *Instrument technicians* maintain the complex instruments and systems in good working order. *Weather analysts* interpret or analyze the day-to-day weather patterns, and *climatologists* summarize and interpret weather records for many different kinds of applications. *Research meteorologists* are needed to insure that new knowledge is continually applied to the weather service's operations. *Librarians, editors, writers,* and *information analysts* supporting the information and publishing activities of the service must often have a scientific background in meteorology. Finally, *management* and *administrative personnel* are needed to direct the weather service as well as to supply the so-called "housekeeping" needs of the agency, such as working space, equipment, personnel, and accounting and payroll services.

These are highly generalized categories. The number of actual positions is much greater, as you can see by looking ahead to Table 2; this table shows job titles and corresponding grades and salaries in 1971. Duties involved in this great diversity of positions will become clearer as we consider how the National Weather Service operates.

OBSERVING, FORECASTING, AND WARNING SERVICES

WHEN THE NATIONAL OCEANIC and Atmospheric Administration came into being on October 3, 1970, the Weather Bureau was renamed the National Weather Service.

The National Weather Service observes and reports the weather of the United States and its possessions. It provides weather forecasts to the general public and issues warnings against tornadoes, hurricanes, floods, and other weather hazards. It also supplies special services to aviation, agriculture, and other activities. A network of observing stations, forecasting offices, and communications lines—in addition to NOAA's aircraft, satellite system, and computers—makes it possible for the Weather Service to carry out these functions. Since modern weather forecasting by computers depends on the largest possible area of observations, reports from many other countries of the world and from the military weather services also contribute to the work of forecasting. Getting weather information to the public is one of the important tasks of personnel at some 300 offices located across the country.

Many of the National Weather Service's 5,000 full-time employees are engaged in the vital tasks of making weather observations and of deriving the basic forecasts and warnings from these observations. More than half of NWS's personnel are occupied in this work, which is called the Basic Weather Service Program because it provides the meteorological information on which all the other services depend. Various specialized tasks are related to particular *weather phenomena*—such as hurricane forecasting—while certain specialized services are related to the particular *needs of the user*—for example, the Agricultural Weather Service. The Public Weather Service, which involves getting the weather information to the public through radio, television, telephone, and teletypewriter, employs about a thousand people. The Aviation Weather Service occupies another 800 people, while the remaining specialized services use only about 300 persons.

The Basic Observation Network provides three types of observations—surface, upper air, and radar—with many stations taking more than one type. *Surface observations* include measurements of air temperature, wind speed and direction, dew point, barometric pressure, sky conditions, cloud height, visibility, and precipitation. About a thousand stations over the United States make such observations, but only 300 are operated by the Weather Service. Personnel of the Federal Aviation Agency, the Coast Guard, and other cooperating agencies man most of the remaining 700. Observers make the measurements hourly throughout the day and night at most stations, and more frequently when required by bad weather. The reports are immediately collected and distributed by teletypewriter.

Upper air observations are of two types—rawinsonde and pilot balloon. The rawinsonde observation is obtained by sending aloft a balloon-borne instrument, the radiosonde, which measures temperature, relative humidity, and pressure. The direction and speed of the upper winds are obtained by tracking the radiosonde with a *radiotheodelite* or by radar. The pilot balloon observations are made by releasing a baloon and tracking it by means of an optical instrument—the theodolite. Upper air observations are taken at more than 150 locations of the National Weather Service and at many additional points by other agencies or cooperating organizations.

With *weather radar,* observers are able to detect and track precipitation areas, thunderstorms, squall lines, hurricanes, and other weather systems, and to obtain measurements of the location, height, and intensity of precipitation. Weather radar operates by sending out a narrow beam of radio energy which is reflected by water droplets. The beam scans the atmosphere either horizontally or vertically, and the *echoes* are displayed on the radarscope to show the patterns, locations, and motion of the rain, snow, or icing area. When precipitation is observed, radar observations are made hourly, or even more frequently when severe storms are indicated. Radar makes it possible for the local weather office to issue short-period forecasts and warnings of severe weather. The Weather Service operates 34 long-range and 58 short-range radars. Surface, upper-air, and radar observations are made, for the most part, by meteorological technicians. However, meteorologists in training positions also assist at the work of observing.

Once the observations are coded, they are either entered directly on the teletypewriter circuit by the observer or turned over to communications personnel of the Federal Aviation Administration. The National Weather Service's reports, together with those from stations all over the world, are collected at the National Meteorological Center in Suitland, Md., and selected reports are distributed to the other offices. At the same location, the National Environmental Satellite Service collects data from NOAA's and NASA's meteorological satellites and prepares it for use in weather analysis and forecasting—the other main function of the Basic Weather Service. This service is accomplished at three levels, or echelons. Generalized weather analyses and forecasts for large areas are produced at the first-echelon offices, which include the National Meteorological Center; the National Severe Storms Forecast Center at Kansas City, Mo.; the National Hurricane Center at Miami; the Hurricane Warning Centers at San Francisco and Honolulu; and the Regional Center for Tropical Meteorology at Miami, which, like NMC, has been assigned a place in the World Weather System by the World Meteorological Organization. The second-echelon offices are the NWS Forecast Offices, of which there will be 50 by 1973. Two forecast offices are currently located at universities having meteorology departments. The third echelon in the forecast organization includes about 200 other locations, called National Weather Service Offices. The manner in which the three levels supplement each other is described below.

One might think of the observing stations and the weather satellites as the "eyes" of NOAA's basic weather system and of the National Meteorological Center (NMC) as the system's "brain." A large part of the Center's operations are automated. As the reports stream in, 40 teletypewriter circuits feed the data directly into computers that check the coded observations and produce an error-free list for the chartmen to use in plotting the maps. These are plotted in sections that can then be assembled for the weather analyst.

As the stream of processed data moves on, a computer linked with a curve follower produces weather maps automatically at various levels in the atmosphere. In the meantime, meteorologists have made manual analyses at several stages as a check on the computer. After the weather observations have been checked and analyzed, the information from a regular network of points on the analyzed maps is fed into the computer, which is programed to produce a forecast chart. The instructions to the machine involve many manipulations resulting from the application of the basic physical equations to the initial data. The forecasts are then prepared automatically for distribution and for input to airline and military flight-planning computers. The upper-air forecasts are distributed without change, but weather analysts manually adjust the predicted surface weather map to show areas of weather and cloudiness, and to check and improve upon the machine forecasts.

Although a great deal of the work at NMC is automated, this does not mean that the Center has little need for people. On the contrary, it employs many highly trained technicians and meteorologists to produce the elaborate and timely forecasts that only the "man-machine mix" has made possible.

The analyses and forecasts made at NMC are distributed by code and also by *facsimile,* a process that reproduces the charts graphically. Thus, all of the work of the Center is almost immediately available to the second echelon of forecasters at the NWS Forecast Offices. These Offices also have the advisories and warnings from the other special forecast centers. Using all this material as "guidance," the forecasters at the FO's prepare state forecasts of general weather conditions and detailed forecasts for zones of five to fifteen thousand square miles. The forecasts are isssued every six hours.

The third-echelon offices not only take weather observations, but prepare localized forecasts adapted from the State and zone forecasts issued by the Forecast Offices, taking into account local topographic and other geographic factors that affect the weather. They also prepare warnings based on known weather hazards, and serve as outlets for the Public Weather Service.

The basic forecast information is adapted in many ways for special purposes. The Aviation Weather Service provides the detailed and frequent weather reports, forecasts, and advisories needed for aviation. In bad weather, the reports determine whether an airport is to be closed; the enroute and terminal forecasts help dispatchers and controllers decide on the best cruise levels, fuel loads, alternate terminals, and other details of flight operation. Under the Agricutural and Fire Weather Services, specially trained meteorologists are located at many Offices to prepare weather forecasts and warnings for agricultural operations and the protection of forests. Farming operations are, of course, especially weather-sensitive: planting, harvesting, and spraying, for example, must be planned for the right weather, and protection from frost may be needed when the temperature is predicted to fall to a certain point. Forecasts of potentially bad fire-weather conditions, such as thunderstorms and very low humidities, are needed for fire control operations. Other specialized forecasts, such as daily air pollution potential advisories, are prepared at many offices to assist local, state, or other federal agencies in preventing dangerous levels of pollution. Under an agreement with the World Meteorological Organization, the United States provides weather services to ships in the western North Atlantic and in the eastern and central North Pacific oceans. Consequently, Forecast Offices at Washington, D.C., San Francisco, and Honolulu prepare marine weather forecasts that are broadcast to ships at sea by the Coast Guard. Some Forecast Offices also prepare coastal and inland waters forecasts for shipping and small craft.

Hydrologic forecasts and services make up another important part of the National Weather Service's warning service. The hydrologist's forecasts depend on networks of precipitation and river-stage reporting stations, and also upon forecasts of temperature and precipitation from the Basic Weather Service. Information on the extent of snow fields is obtained from the weather satellites, while the location, extent, and intensity of rainfall can be estimated from radar observations. Thus the hydrologist's work is closely dependent on that of the meteorologist. Much of the work in the Office of Hydrology, in fact, is conducted by *hydrometeorologists*. (In the United States, hydrometeorology refers to that part of meteorology which is of direct concern to hydrology.) A Weather Service Office in each river district is designated as a River District Office to maintain the river and rainfall network and collect the necessary observations. At River Forecast Centers, professional hydrologists prepare short-range, 30-day, and long-range, seasonal river forecasts that are disseminated locally by the River District Offices.

Another activity of the NWS is the space operations support it provides to NASA and the Department of Defense, including global forecasts, weather briefing for actual spaceflights, and a variety of observations and consulting services. Sections of the Space Support Group work at Suitland, Maryland, with the NMC, and at Cape Kennedy, Miami, and Houston.

CLIMATOLOGICAL SERVICES

NOAA'S CLIMATOLOGICAL SERVICES and research are concentrated mainly in the National Environmental Data Service (EDS). EDS operates national data centers for a number of the geophysical disciplines, including the National Climatic Center at Asheville, N. C., archiving and processing the data in various ways. It also publishes many different kinds of local, national, and world climatological summaries and atlases, as well as the printed *Daily Weather Map, Weekly Series,* the *Mariners Weather Log,* and the *Catalog of Meteorological Satellite Data.* Since these publications offer maps and data for study, term projects, and graduate research, the meteorology student usually becomes familiar with them early in his career. Providing data and analyses for research is one of the important functions of the Data Service, but climatology also rivals weather forecasting as one of the large applied fields of meteorology. Hence, supplying expert advice, or consulting, is another important aspect of the Data Service's programs.

Climatological data are collected from four primary sources. Hourly reports from the Weather Service's and the Federal Aviation Administration's 610 surface observing stations are one source. More than 200 stations provide upper air data. About 12,000 volunteer weather observers in the United States make daily readings of precipitation, and 5,000 of these observe the daily maximum and minimum temperatures. There are another thousand special-purpose and public-service stations providing supplementary data. EDS, from its Headquarters Office co-located with the National Weather Service, manages the climatological network of cooperative stations.

It is an interesting sidelight that in the early days of our country, quite a few famous individuals, including Thomas

Jefferson, were systematic "volunteer" weather observers. Thus the National Climatic Center's holdings range from the contents of eighteenth century journals to the more than 100 million observations collected annually from all over the globe. In addition to providing routine, published summaries, the Center makes many special climatological studies for other federal agencies, private firms, and individual citizens.

Under the Field Services Program, state climatologists offer a state-based consultant service in the varied applications of climatology. The state climatologist—and also the regional climatologist located at a National Weather Service Regional Office—is an expert in the climate of his area of responsibility. The expert's key task is to work with local or state organizations, frequently through the state university or colleges, and to assist these organizations in solving problems that have an impact on the area's economy. For example, he may provide data to engineers for use in the design and layout of buildings or to agricultural county agents for application to farm problems. Forty-four state and six regional climatologists serve the 50 states and Puerto Rico.

SATELLITE METEOROLOGY

THE NATIONAL ENVIRONMENTAL SATELLITE SERVICE combines operations and research functions. It operates the National Operational Meteorological Satellite System and prepares the cloud and radiation data from the satellites for use by the Weather Service. As the satellite's television cameras scan the atmosphere below, the pictures they make are distorted because of the slant view and because of the Earth's curvature. These pictures have to be "rectified," mapped in proper perspective, and joined together in "mosaics" to be useful. The pictures are prepared in this way by computer techniques, and are now being transmitted experimentally to countries all over the world by communications satellites. In a recent two-year period, more than 100 tropical cyclones were spotted and tracked from satellite cloud pictures.

Two kinds of spacecraft are used in the environmental satellite system: *polar-orbiting* and *geostationary*. The polar-orbiting NOAA satellites revolve around the Earth, from pole to pole, while the Earth rotates beneath them. Thus the satellite observes the Earth both in daylight and darkness, supplying world-wide observations by visual means in daylight and by infrared photography at night. The Applications Technology Satellites (ATS), revolving in an equatorial orbit at the same angular speed at which the Earth rotates, appear stationary with respect to the Earth beneath. They are positioned above the equator at an elevation of 22,300 miles, and their cameras view a large disc of the Earth at 15- to 30-minute intervals. Some of the operational satellites carry camera systems that automatically transmit pictures to ground stations within range, so that regional data are available almost immediately. Others provide global data by storing the pictures until they can be transmitted to one of the more elaborate Command and Data Acquisition Stations for central processing.

The Satellite Service also develops new techniques for acquiring data and applying it to geophysical problems. Many advances have been made in the decade since the first pictures of the Earth's cloud systems were sent back by TIROS I on April 1, 1960. These developments have resulted in a fairly thorough integration of the satellite observations into the National Weather Service's Basic Weather System. Many of the satellite's capabilities are expected to be further incorporated into the World Weather System and into the Global Atmospheric Research Program that will occupy many meteorologists during the 1970s. The satellite is capable of making observations of cloudiness and of the temperature distribution in the atmosphere, all over the world. It can interrogate other observation systems, track balloons to determine wind direction and speed, and communicate weather observations very rapidly over great distances.

In 1969, after years of preparatory research, using data from the newly launched research satellite Nimbus 3, meteorologists of the Satellite Service were able to show a most impressive contribution to weather analysis and forecasting. This consisted of graphs showing the distribution of temperature with height through the atmosphere, similar to the data obtained from the radiosonde instruments described earlier. Radiosonde observations require very elaborate equipment at each station where the sounding is made. The satellite was able to make a sounding wherever the sky was partly clear, and research was expected to remove the difficulty of cloud cover. The new technique represents a great advance in observing the atmosphere, and in a short time the data from Nimbus 3 were being used, particularly over ocean areas where there are few upper-air observations, to help NMC prepare the upper-air maps that are vital to accurate forecasting. The temperature observations are obtained from measurements of infrared radiation received at seven different wavelengths from the atmosphere below the satellite.

RESEARCH ACTIVITIES

ALTHOUGH SOME RESEARCH is carried out in NOAA's operating components (for example, in the National Weather Service's Techniques Development Laboratory), the basic research effort is concentrated largely in the Environmental Research Laboratories. Most of the Laboratories, which have

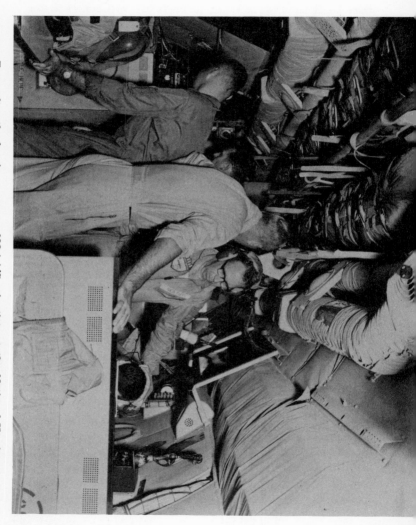

Even after the hurricane season NOAA'S scientists at the National Hurricane Research Lab in Miami study the big storms. This is the interior of a weather research airplane that will be used in Project Stormfury—the NOAA-Navy joint experiment to see if hurricanes can be modified.
Courtesy of ESSA

their headquarters in Boulder, Colorado, work either wholly or to some extent on meteorological problems. Examples of the kind of research accomplished at the individual Laboratories are indicated below.

The National Hurricane Research Laboratory at Miami, Fla., studies hurricanes and other tropical weather phenomena. It is co-located with the Regional Center for Tropical Meteorology and the National Hurricane Center and makes considerable use of ERL's Research Flight Facility, also at Miami, to collect detailed data on tropical storms. Under Project Stormfury, in cooperation with the Navy and the Air Force, the Hurricane Research Laboratory is experimenting with the modification of hurricanes by seeding the tall "wall cloud," around the center of the eye of the storm, with silver iodide. The Laboratory conducts many basic studies aimed at furthering our understanding of tropical cyclones and predicting them more accurately.

At Norman, Oklahoma, the National Severe Storms Laboratory studies data from aircraft, satellites, an instrumented tower, radar, and a close network of observing stations to learn more about the nature of thunderstorms, squall lines, and tornadoes. Relatively little is known about the inner structure of tornadoes, and doppler radar is expected to add to our knowledge of the motions within these storms. The doppler radar gives information about particle motions because the return signal reflected from the moving target differs slightly from the transmitted signal.

The Atmospheric Physics and Chemistry Laboratory, at Boulder and Miami, makes studies of the composition of the atmosphere and the physics of clouds and precipitation. Using the facilities of Project Stormfury, and in other experiments, the Laboratory has been able to identify the cumulus clouds that can be seeded with a good probability of increasing their size and the rainfall they produce. The experiments have given considerable theoretical and experimental support to weather modification activities.

The Geophysical Fluid Dynamics Laboratory, located at Princeton University, does basic research on the dynamics and physics of the atmosphere and ocean. Its scientists develop mathematical models of the atmosphere and ocean that can be used to predict changes in the circulation and weather patterns. By starting with basic data like the composition of the atmosphere, the distribution of energy from the sun, and the location of land and water bodies, GFDL meteorologists have been able to reproduce the general climatic patterns of the Earth. Using models like this, they hope to be able to determine the causes of changes in the Earth's climate, such as those associated with the Ice Age. The heat, gases, and particles poured into the atmosphere by power plants, refineries, and other industrial activities affect local climates and the possibilities of widespread climatic effects need to be better understood.

The Air Resources Laboratory at Silver Spring, Maryland, and various field locations, conducts laboratory and field experiments to develop better methods for predicting and controlling air pollution. A cooperative program involving ARL, the Nationol Center for Atmospheric Research, several universities, the Environmental Protection Agency, and other government organizations was begun in 1970. This program is aimed at determining the impact of cities on the atmosphere, and it is significant because it marks a comprehensive attack by the government, the universities, and private institutions on one of the most critical problems of our society.

The Aeronomy Laboratory, at Boulder, Colorado, studies the physical and chemical processes of the ionosphere and exosphere of the Earth and other planets, and the Wave Propagation

Laboratory makes studies aimed at *remote sensing* of the environment, also at Boulder. Remote sensing refers to techniques for observing at a distance, as with radar or with the radiation-measuring instruments on satellites.

Research scientists at the Atlantic Oceanographic Laboratory in Miami study the highly important energy exchanges between the ocean and the atmosphere, and have been active in one of the most striking large-scale field experimnts in recent years—the Barbados Oceanographic and Meteorological Experiment (BOMEX). Not only NOAA but many other civil and military groups were involved in BOMEX. Ships, aircraft, and satellites were used to study the transfer of energy, momentum, and water vapor between the atmosphere and ocean east of Barbados. The experiment was the first cooperative effort of the Global Atmospheric Research Program (Chapter 2). The scientific significance of BOMEX is that, in order to extend the period of numerical forecasts beyond a few days, the forecast models must take account of the energy transferred from the warm ocean to the cooler atmosphere above.

CAREERS IN NOAA

CAREER LADDERS for meteorologists in the civil service are essentially of two kinds: one culminating in work that is primarily scientific or technical and the other in positions that are mainly administrative or managerial. However, in the upper grades, even the technical and research positions usually involve some aspects of management; and top management positions may go only to individuals highly qualified in the science. Both types of jobs are represented in Table 2. The nearly 40 different positions listed in this table suggest the diversity of careers open to meteorologists in NOAA.

In general, a variety of assignments in a meteorologist's career not only helps him select an area of specialization but provides a good background for the specialization itself. Mobility is an important factor in advancement, for the needs of the agency and the corresponding career opportunities are likely to occur in many different regions. Experience in international assignments may prove helpful to an individual's career, for many meteorological problems, both operational and scientific, have global implications. Some senior meteorologists spend much time at international meetings on one or another aspect of such problems. The World Meteorological Organization has occasional openings for experienced meteorologists in training or consulting jobs in many countries of the world and in administrative and technical positions at the WMO Secretariat in Geneva. After several years' experience in the United States, an individual might advantageously consider one of these or a similar assignment.

The typical duties of meteorologists and meteorological technicians are closely related to the main service, operational, and research programs touched on in the earlier sections of this chapter. For the career-minded, the organizational setup of the National Weather Service is also of some interest. For administration and management, the National Weather Service has a Headquarters Office (traditionally known in the Weather Service as the "Central Office") located at Silver Spring, Maryland. Regional Offices patterned somewhat after the Central Office— each having a division concerned with scientific services, operations, and administrative and technical services—are located in Garden City, New York; Fort Worth, Texas; Kansas City, Missouri; Salt Lake City, Utah; Anchorage, Alaska; and Honolulu, Hawaii.

The basic qualifications for beginning a professional career in meteorology in the civil service, at the GS-5 or GS-7 level, is a B.S. degree in meteorology. Acceptable also is any bachelor's degree with at least 20 semester hours of meteorology, including 6 semester hours each in synoptic and dynamic meteorology; 6 semester hours in differential and integral calculus; and 6 semester hours in physics. Graduate work or additional experience may qualify applicants for higher grade positions.

Many meteorologists start their careers at field stations that provide both general services and one or more of the specialized services discussed earlier. General service duties may include supplying local forecasts to radio and television stations and answering requests from the public. Specialized services may include briefing aircraft pilots on weather conditions, issuing and distributing "watches" or "warnings" of hazardous weather conditions, and providing special types of weather information. Although weather observations are normally made by technicians, meteorologists may sometimes make observations of a special nature. The meteorologist in training may be assigned to make studies of local forecast problems and to specialized training details. After several years of experience and training, he usually moves into specialized work, such as central analysis and prediction, mathematical analysis and programming, aviation forecasting, radar meteorology, satellite meteorology, climatology, agricultural meteorology, fire weather forecasting, spaceflight meteorology, marine forecasting, or hydrology. Increasingly broad and specialized experience, accompanied by graduate study, will eventually equip him for staff or supervisory positions or for research in a specialized area. Most research positions require graduate study.

In a general way, the duties of research meteorologists in the civil service can be understood from the earlier account of typical studies being carried on in the Research Laboratories. NOAA's research meteorologists are located at Silver Spring,

Maryland, Boulder, Colorado, Kansas City, Missouri, Norman, Oklahoma, Cincinnati, Ohio, Las Vegas, Nevada, Miami, Florida, Idaho Falls, Idaho, Oak Ridge, Tennessee, Raleigh, North Carolina, Princeton, New Jersey, and a few other locations. Research meteorologists work regular hours, as a rule. They may work at field experiments, in laboratories in which the experimental equipment is a wind tunnel or an electronic computer, or at desks. Research careers are discussed at further length in Chapter 6.

The field station at which a meteorologist works is typically, but not always, located at an airport. The stations are quite varied in size and function. One may be staffed by as few as ten, whereas another may have more than 100 people, including meteorological and electronic technicians as well as meteorologists. The operation of each major office is directed by a Meteorologist in Charge, who maintains liaison with local officials, officials of other agencies, radio and television stations, and newspaper editors. Except when there is a shortage of personnel, the MIC usually works an eight-hour day, five days a week. Stations demanding less scientific competence may be directed by an Official in Charge, who is a meteorological technician instead of a meteorologist.

The weather operations at the various offices may range from limited observations and briefings to a full-scale program with comprehensive observations, international aviation forecasting, and marine, agricultural, and other forecast responsibilities. Most forecast offices operate 24 hours a day, seven days a week. However, all employees receive additional pay for night work between 6 p.m. and 6 a.m.; for overtime work in excess of 40 hours a week; and for work on holidays.

At the National Meteorological Center, a meteorologist might participate in programing meteorological problems for the computer, or help predict changes in the wind field, the temperature field, or moisture patterns. Research in the NWS is of the applied or developmental type, as a rule, and much of it is related to forecasting problems.

Climatologists ordinarily work regular hours. The increased use of automatic data processing requires a relatively strong mathematical and statistical background. The state climatologist frequently has his office at a state university and sometimes combines teaching and research with his consultant duties. The largest concentration of climatologists is in Asheville, North Carolina, and in the Headquarters Office at Silver Spring, Maryland.

Satellite meteorologists perform such work as the daily processing of satellite data, either subjectively or by computer methods. They develop methods for applying the data to weather analysis, methods of interpreting radiation data, and instruments for remote sensing of the atmosphere, such as that developed for Nimbus 3, described earlier. They do basic research on various scales of atmospheric phenomena, using satellite data, and develop techniques such as that involved in rectifying satellite pictures. Most of this work is performed at the National Environmental Satellite Center at Suitland, Maryland.

The advantages of working as a meteorologist in the civil service are numerous. As we mentioned in Chapter 3, NOAA has an active training program that includes full-time university assignments, off-duty course work, and duty hours study. When off-duty courses are related to an employee's work, the government can pay tuition and other benefits. Among other advantages of a career in NOAA are the relative stability of government employment and quite liberal leave, retirement, insurance, and health plans. Salaries are geared to a position-classification system that relates pay to the skill, education, experience, and responsibility demanded in the job.

TABLE 2

*Career Ladder for Meteorologists and Hydrologists in NOAA
Entrance Salaries in 1971*

Typical Positions	Civil Service Grade	Percentage in Grade	Entrance Salary
Meteorologist Trainees	GS-5	5%	$8,324
General Service Meteorologist in Hydrology, Forecasting, Pilot Briefing, Agriculture, Public Service, Research	GS-7		$10,298
Radar Meteorologists, Flight Briefing Officers, Hydrologists, Public Service Meteorologists, Fire Weather Forecasters, Meteorological Analysts, Agricultural Meteorologists, Meteorologist in Charge, Principal Assistant, Marine Reporting Officers, Fruit-Frost Forecasters	GS-9	16%	$11,517
Zone Forecasters, Research Meteorologists, Fire Weather Forecasters, Meteorological Analysts, Research Forecasters, Hydrologists, Space Flight Meteorologists, Upper-Air Specialists, Meteorologist in Charge, Principal Assistant, Storm Tide Forecasters, Agricultural Meteorologists, Marine Reporting Officers, Public Service Meteorologists, Chief Airport Meteorologists	GS-11	25%	$12,615
Radar Meteorologists, General Weather Forecasters, Research Forecasters, River Forecasters, Research Meteorologists, Water	GS-12	28%	$15,040

Typical Positions	*Civil Service Grade*	*Percentage in Grade*	*Entrance Salary*
Supply Forecasters, Agricultural Meteorologists, Spaceflight Meteorologists, Hydrologists, Aviation Forecasters, Meteorologist in Charge, Principal Assistant, Supervisory Positions, Section Chiefs, Chief Airport Meteorologists, Storm Tide Forecasters, State Climatologists			
Associate Directors, Regional Directors, Division Chiefs,			
Assistant Division Chiefs, River Forecasters, Branch Chiefs,	GS-13	15%	$17,761
Hydrologic Engineers, Meteorologist in Charge of Forecast	GS-14	6%	$20,815
Centers, Spaceflight Meteorologists, Project Directors,	GS-15	3%	$24,251
Supervisory Positions, Aviation Forecasters, Guidance Forecasters, Chief Airport Meteorologists, Research Forecasters, Regional Climatologists, Research Meteorologists, Laboratory Directors	GS-16 and above	2%	$28,129

CHAPTER 5

METEOROLOGY IN THE MILITARY SERVICES

METEOROLOGY IS UNUSUAL among the scientific professions in the United States in that fully one-third of its members serve in the military arm of the federal government. The Army has relatively few officers in meteorology, since weather support for the Army's operations is provided by the Air Force, but the Army does carry on research and development in atmospheric science. Personnel at U.S. Coast Guard stations also make weather observations, and the Coast Guard supplies the ships that, in cooperation with the National Weather Service, maintain six ocean weather stations in the North Atlantic and Pacific oceans. However, military meteorology is overwhelmingly concentrated in the Air Force's Air Weather Service and in the Naval Weather Service. Over 2,000 professional meteorologists work as weather officers in these two services, while their enlisted personnel number more than 11,000.

More than 10,000 personnel are assigned to Air Weather Service, and approximately 3,000 are in the Naval Weather Service. Both services also employ some civilian meteorologists.

Although the basic missions of the Air and Naval Weather Services are to provide weather support for U.S. military forces, their unique facilities on the ground, in the air, and at sea are used in many ways to supplement civilian meteorological services and research. Examples of this cooperation in civil functions are the military's weather reconnaissance activities and their participation in such large field experiments as BOMEX and Project Stormfury (Chapter 4).

THE AIR WEATHER SERVICE

THE PRIMARY MISSION of the Air Weather Service (AWS) is to supply weather and environmental support and advice for operations of the U.S. Air Force and U.S. Army around the world. However, AWS also provides "environmental support" to other agencies of the Department of Defense and other federal agencies. For example, in addition to the more routine operations of weather observing and forecasting, the Air Weather Service is active in atmospheric sampling and aerial weather reconnaissance, in sounding the atmosphere by means of rockets, and in monitoring and predicting space disturbances—services that are vital to agencies like the Atomic Energy Commission, the National Oceanic and Atmospheric Administration, and the National Aeronautics and Space Administration.

The headquarters of the Air Weather Service is located at Scott Air Force Base, Illinois. Faced with providing land and air weather support on a global basis, AWS collects observations from ground stations strategically located all over the world. It makes use of the basic weather services provided by NOAA and is involved in the World Meteorological Organization. It has more than 10,000 highly trained technical people, and the weather stations in its network number nearly 275, located in 24 countries and islands. About 69 percent of its officers are assigned in the continental United States, 20 percent in Hawaii and the Pacific theatre, and 11 percent in the European theatre.

Where it is impractical to operate ground weather stations, the AWS meets it needs by aerial weather reconnaissance. About 2,600 individuals are engaged in this work, of whom about 50 are weather officers on flying status, providing a somewhat unusual interdisciplinary occupation. The specially instrumented aircraft of AWS reconnaissance squadrons fly about 53,000 miles every day, and make thousands of observations annually along their routes. Flying over vast areas of the oceans, at intervals they release sounding devices called *dropsondes*. The dropsonde, supported by a parachute that lets the instrument drift to the surface, transmits signals denoting pressure, temperature, and humidity back to the aircraft. This information is immediately relayed to ground control stations where the soundings are checked and retransmitted to all weather units via teletypewriter circuits.

Observing and tracking tropical cyclones in the Atlantic and the Pacific areas is one of the more spectacular missions of Air Force weather reconnaissance. Aircraft of the 53rd Weather Reconnaissance Squadron, known as the Hurricane Hunters, operate out of Ramey AFB, Puerto Rico. The Typhoon Chasers of the 54th WRS (Andersen AFB, Guam) reconnoiter western Pacific storms, while crews of the 55th WRS (McClellan AFB, Calif.) cover the eastern Pacific. When there is evidence of a storm in the Atlantic or Pacific area, the National Hurricane Center in Miami, the Typhoon Center on Guam, or the San Francisco Hurricane Office alerts the flying weathermen. The reconnaissance job is then to locate the storm, fly to its center or *eye,* and determine the storm's characteristics. A key man in the six-man crew is the weather observer. He records the data by means of which the navigator is able to guide the flight to the storm's vicinity. With help from the radar and from the weather observer, the navigator is then able to locate the eye of the storm. Since the eye is virtually cloud-free, it can be detected by the absence of raindrop echoes on the radar screen. Flying through the storm's wall cloud to its center, the crew encounter clouds and rain so dense as to shroud the wingtips, and, at times, very heavy turbulence. Using radar, the crew then fly the assigned track profile back to the edge of the storm, circle it to gather more data, make another penetration fix (fuel permitting), and return home. In 1969, it was an AWS WC-130 that entered Hurricane Camille, the most intense Atlantic hurricane of record, and provided the advance information that saved many lives.

The space environmental support facility of the AWS provides information for communications and space activities of the Air Force. Some disturbances of the sun, such as solar flares, produce radio blackouts and dangerous energetic-particle radiation that can damage or destroy sensitive electronic or photographic equipment and even kill an unprotected man in space. To observe and predict solar emissions that might be hazardous to men or instruments, the AWS operates a solar observing network of optical and radio telescopes spaced around the world to keep the sun under nearly 24-hour surveillance.

The more routine tasks of the AWS, though perhaps less spectacular than flying into hurricanes and observing solar "weather," can nevertheless be exciting and vitally important. Examples of how weather affects military oprations are almost endless. To the F-106 pilot returning from an intercept mission with 30 minutes of fuel left, low ceilings and visibilities at his home base are a real threat. Clear-air turbulence may prevent air-to-air refueling of aircraft short of fuel. To the reconnaissance pilot, a deck of clouds hiding a valley and forcing him to fly where enemy radar can see him is just as real a threat as antiaircraft fire. To the ground crew refueling an aircraft, the enemy may be a thunderstorm just west of the base. For the maintenance crew working on the bleak Dakota prairies, a blizzard sweeping out of Canada can turn a routine job into a fight for survival. Practically very facet of modern military operations is weather dependent: troop movements, strategic and tactical air support, photo reconnaissance, missile launching, and space flights. Thus, the Air Weather Service plays a vital and interesting role in almost every activity of the Air Force and the Army.

The work of the Air Weather Service is divided into six task areas: observing, reporting, analyzing, and forecasting the weather; modifying it where feasible; and giving weather advice to clients.

More than half of the Air Weather Service's personnel are engaged in observing, i.e., in making surface, upper-air, aerial reconnaissance, and space observations. Most observing is done by technical rather than by professional personnel, by airmen rather than by weather officers. Observations are made at some 230 Air Force and Army airfields, and most of these operate 24 hours a day. All observing locations supporting air operations have electronic meteorological instrumentation for measuring cloud height, visibility, temperature-humidity, and wind velocity, which are positioned for each runway. AWS also operates upper-air observing stations, including 20 mobile units, as well as 127 weather search radars. In addition to hunting tropical cyclones, the reconnaissance squadrons monitor the composition of the upper air and provide weather information for the launching and splashdown of space ships. For its air sampling program, the AWS also uses large helium-filled balloons that are launched to altitudes up to 25 miles. To obtain observations at even higher altitudes, the AWS operates a network of seven rocket-sonde stations, spaced around the northern hemisphere, which measure temperature, density, and wind at altitudes in excess of 50 miles. AWS obtains data from the NOAA satellites by means of its automatic picture transmission (APT) receivers. Satellite data are highly useful in making operational decisions and identifying areas for aerial refueling, reconnaissance, and air-craft recovery.

The AWS has centralized facilities for weather analysis and forecasting at the Air Force Global Weather Central at Offutt AFB, Nebraska, and at regional centers in England and Japan. With the aid of large computers, the Global Weather Central is able to make use of advanced numerical forecasting techniques and thus to provide analyses and forecasts for the entire globe. In addition to the weather centrals, there are mission support centers such as the Tactical Air Command forecast center at Langley AFB, Virginia. There are also a number of specialized centers such as the Joint Typhoon Warning Center at Guam; this one is operated in conjunction with the Naval Weather Service. The Aerospace Environmental Support Center in the NORAD Cheyenne Mountain complex at Colorado Springs, Colorado, is the hub of the solar observing and forecasting network. Data from the observing sites are received here around the clock and plotted and analyzed by solar forecasters, who prepare summaries and 27-day predictions of solar activity.

The task of weather analysis and forecasting is not com-pletely concentrated in the weather centrals. Forecasters in the field, regardless of the size of the unit, use the centralized analyses and predictions to make more specific and localized forecasts for operations and to brief and advise military commanders.

Providing weather communications is a function of the Air Force Communications Service. However, because of AWS's complete dependence on the rapid movement of weather information, many of its personnel have become experts in the communications field. A communications service pioneered by AWS is the pilot-to-forecaster service, which makes possible a highly useful exchange of weather observations and advisory services.

In weather modification, the primary emphasis of AWS is on the dissipation of supercooled fog at airfields. Supercooled fog is composed of water droplets at temperatures below freezing. With the onset of such fog, the seeding aircraft flies over and dispenses Dry Ice. In about forty-five minutes, the fog dissipates to the point at which aircraft can safely take off and land. During the 1968-69 fog season, the AWS was able to open Elmendorf AFB, Alaska, for 180 arrivals and 180 departures that otherwise would have been delayed, diverted, or cancelled.

Advising the men who make operational decisions is AWS's final task. Through its staff meteorologists, the Service tries to insure that environmental factors are incorporated at an early stage in all systems, command and control procedures, and operational programs. Each commander gets weather support developed and designed for his specific mission.

CAREERS IN THE AIR WEATHER SERVICE

TO ACCOMPLISH ITS TASKS, the Air Weather Service must have a body of highly-trained professional weather officers. Currently (1970), the AWS requires about 230 graduates in meteorology each year. This number includes 175 from the basic meteorology program of the Air Force Reserve Officers Training Corps (AFROTC) and the Officer Training School (OTS); 50 from the master's program; and 5 from the Ph.D. program. Of the approximately 1,650 AWS authorized officers in grades of lieutenant through brigadier general, about 580 require advanced degrees. These needs for professionally trained officers can be effectively met only through extensive educational and training programs and, as a result, educational opportunities in the Air Weather Service constitute one of the most obvious advantages of the career weather officer.

Each year, graduates of AFROTC are selected to take meteorology at several civilian universities (see Chapter 3). These individuals, upon successful completion of 9-month to one-year courses in basic meteorology, supply the bulk of the officers for AWS. The basic meteorology course, plus previous college work, gives the equivalent of a B.S. in Meteorology or, alternatively, credit toward a master's degree. The chances for attending graduate school are considered to be very good. Graduate education is almost assured for those with acceptable academic standing, good performance as a weather officer, and the desire to return to school. Weather officers are eligible to return to the civilian university for graduate-level study after about 36 months' active duty. Approximately 45 percent of the officers who remain in the Service return to school for a master's degree. When an officer is assigned to school, he receives full tuition, a book allowance, and his regular basic pay and other allowances. As an example, in 1970 an Air Force captain assigned to a university for study received a salary of $11,050 annually in addition to his school expenses.

Officers who attend the basic meteorology course are assigned to the Air Weather Service. Because the Service is small, it is able to give each officer personalized, individual consideration for assignment. Since there are nearly 400 installations, the chances of getting assigned to the area of an individual's choice is quite good. However, personnel must be assigned in accordance with operational needs. Except for volunteers, AWS tries to assign basic meteorology graduates to continental United States locations.

The opportunities for promotion in the Service are excellent. Some 40 generals have spent parts of their careers in AWS. In the grades of major and lieutenant colonel, the AWS has generally exceeded the promotional averages of the Air Force, one reason being that weather officers are better educated than the average Air Force officer and assume commands at an earlier age. Many captains with less than four years' service are detachment commanders supervising base weather stations. Salaries, allowances, and other benefits are the same as those for other military personnel of similar rank. Examples of military basic salaries, which like Civil Service salaries are now periodically adjusted by the Executive Department of the federal government, are given in the discussion of Naval Weather Service careers in Chapter 5.

Interested individuals may become career weather officers in any one of several ways. These ways are discussed in Chapter 9.

THE NAVAL WEATHER SERVICE

THE MISSION of the Naval Weather Service is to provide meteorological services for air, surface, and subsurface operations of the U.S. Navy and to provide oceanographic forecasts for all the Armed Forces in support of military plans and operations. Since the operations of the Navy span the Earth, so, too, must

During the hurricane season, National Hurricane Center at Miami, Fla., maintains a 24-hour vigil of the big storms. Using advanced weather forecasting methods and equipment—satellite pictures, radar and flying Hurricane Hunters—it supplies the advisories and warnings for U.S. hurricane territory. It also serves the entire Caribbean neighborhood of nations.

Courtesy of ESSA

the Naval Weather Service, in order to offer adequate environmental support. This support is aimed not only at minimizing the effects of unfavorable conditions, but also at helping the operating forces take advantage of favorable weather and sea conditions.

Considering its worldwide responsibility for forecasting in an environment extending from the deep ocean to the upper atmosphere, the Naval Weather Service is rather small. It consists of about 425 officers, 2,300 enlisted members, and 400 civilian personnel. During peace time the Naval Weather Service shares in the global exchange of observations provided by the nations of the World Meteorological Organization; however, the Navy's highly specialized needs require that it operate its own functional weather service. The heart of this service is the integrated Fleet Weather Central System, consisting of six Weather Centrals and nine Weather Facilities. This system is augmented by smaller weather service units both on shore and on vessels. The Weather Centrals are the principal collectors and processors of meteorological and oceanographic data. The Facilities support the Centrals but have, in addition, many varied special tasks. At the smaller units, weather service personnel interpret information received from the larger offices for local use. Some of the tasks of weather officers and enlisted men are suggested in the following remarks about the Naval Weather Service's operations and functions.

The Fleet Numerical Weather Central at Monterey, California, is a vital part of the system. Operational weather materials are prepared by computers at this Central and transmitted at the rate of 4,000 words per minute directly to computers in the major Weather Centrals. Entire Northern Hemisphere charts can be transmitted in seconds. The Weather Centrals, in turn, collect data from their areas and feed it directly from teletypewriter circuits to computers, where the data are checked for garbles, errors, or duplicates and then speeded to the large computer at the Numerical Weather Central. Computers there are used to prepare forecasts in much the same way as at the National Meterological Center (see Chapter 4). Environmental information can be fed directly into the Navy's system for computerized control of its operations, where it can be recalled at will. Because of the Navy's need for information about both the air and the sea, the Fleet Numerical Weather Central has pioneered in prediction models that treat the atmosphere and the ocean as a single environmental system—an approach that theoretical meteorologists recognize as necessary because of the exchange of energy and momentum (or motion) between the air and the sea.

From Monterey, the forecast maps and other materials are sent to computer sites at Guam, Pearl Harbor, Norfolk, and Rota in Spain. At these points, the data are tailored to meet area requirements and distributed by remote line-drawing and printing equipment to Yokosuka in Japan, Sangley Point in the Philippines, and to London, England.

For antisubmarine warfare requirements, data transmitted to the Fleet include the sea state, sea surface temperatures, and the speed of sound at various depths. The local meteorologist updates the data for the operating area and provides detailed charts. At some air stations supporting antisubmarine warfare (ASW) aircraft, weather personnel prepare briefing folders, while in ASW task groups and in some carrier task groups the meteorological officer gives tailored briefings to the staffs.

Submarines require environmental support both in launching their own weapons, such as *Polaris* missiles, and in avoiding detection by the enemy. Surface winds, the change in temperature with height, sea state, and sea ice conditions are important factors to be considered in launching a *Polaris* missile. Under conditions of poor visibility, strong winds, heavy seas, or considerable low cloud cover, a submarine is extremely difficult to locate. The change in temperature with distance is important, since it affects sonar patterns.

Aircraft operations are probably more dependent upon the weather than any other phase of naval warfare. The feasibility of launching, the effectiveness and endurance of the flight once launched, the recovery in the case of carrier aircraft—all are dependent upon weather information. Enroute winds must be forecast in order to determine if it is possible to reach an assigned target and return. Weather conditions must be suitable for the recovery of the planes. Weather Service personnel aboard carriers and at air stations have to supply timely information to squadron and ship commanders to aid them in making decisions.

Surface ships of all types and sizes require weather support, and hardly a weather factor can be omitted. Sea state and sea temperature affect the capability of sonar as well as the maneuverability of ships. Winds affect not only the state of the sea but, in addition to operations already mentioned, they also affect other military factors such as radiological fallout patterns. Temperatures are important for ballistic settings, fuel consumption, and types of clothing used. Radical temperature and humidity changes aloft will influence radar and radio propagation.

Amphibious operations require more extensive all-around environmental support than does any other naval operation. Sea conditions determine the feasibility of putting men and boats over the side, and surf conditions dictate whether or not they can be landed. Some weather conditions, such as fog, can limit or stop the entire action. Cloud cover may restrict or prevent support. The task force meteorologist must advise the commander of all the many environmental factors that might influence the operation.

The Naval Weather Service, in addition to operating a system for collecting, analyzing, and interpreting weather and oceanographic information, also makes observations where they are needed and provides a number of specialized operations and services. It participates with the National Oceanic and Atmospheric Administration in experiments designed to test the possibility of modifying hurricanes (Project Stormfury, Chapter 4), and like the Air Weather Service carries out weather reconnaissance of hurricanes and typhoons. It conducts ice reconnaissance and forecasting, vital services for ships providing logistic support to polar bases. Observers map the ice and prepare pictorial presentations showing the concentration, size, stage of development, and topography of the ice; from these observations and other environmental data, forecasters prepare their predictions of ice movement. Another operations program employs special techniques for selecting the best predicted routes for ships. Factors considered in making these forecasts (called optimum track ship routing) are wind speed and direction; the height, period, and direction of waves; and ship performance. The objectives of the service are to minimize crossing time, damage to ship and cargo, and passenger discomfort.

CAREERS IN THE NAVAL WEATHER SERVICE

THE NAVAL WEATHER SERVICE'S approximately 425 officers have grades ranging from Ensign through Rear Admiral. All officers are college graduates and about one-third hold advanced degrees in meteorology or related fields. While candidates with a degree in meteorology from an accredited college become qualified rapidly for weather work, other candidates who attend Officers Candidate School may be selected for the Special

Meteorology Course at the Naval Postgraduate School; the latter must have a degree from an accredited college, math through calculus, and one and one-half years of physics. Graduates with a background in oceanography, physics, math, atmospheric or geophysical science, or any engineering course may qualify for meteorological training. Prospective Naval Weather Service Officers receive 16 weeks of training at the Naval Officer Candidate School in Newport, Rhode Island. Those with a degree in meteorology are then immediately assigned to a Fleet Weather Central or Weather Facility. The other selectees attend the special one-year course at the Naval Postgraduate School before being designated meteorologists.

All Naval officers are afforded the opportunity of indicating their personal preference for future duty. Assignment Officers, called detailers, attempt to match vacant billets with individual preferences; however, in making assignments, the needs of the Service have to be considered first. Initial assignments are ordinarily to one of the Fleet Weather Centrals or Facilities.

An important advantage offered Naval Weather Service Officers, in the grade of Lieutenant Junior Grade to Lieutenant Commander, is the opportunity to study for an advanced degree at the Naval Postgraduate School. Selection for postgraduate education depends primarily on academic qualifications and performance in preceding assignments. Officers selected for postgraduate training must agree to extend their obligated service by one year for each six months of schooling. One or two meteorological officers are ordinarily selected each year for doctoral studies at a civilian college or university.

The Naval Postgraduate School at Monterey is a fully accredited institution of higher learning that offers three curricula in meteorology and closely related sciences. The General Meteorology Curriculum is a two-year program designed to prepare officers to become qualified meteorologists with a working knowledge of oceanography as applied to naval operations. Including instruction in high-speed digital computer operations and techniques, with applications to meteorological operations, the course offers an opportunity to attain a Bachelor of Science degree in meteorology. The Advanced Meteorology Curriculum covers much the same material but differs in the mathematical requirements and the depth at which the dynamical and physical aspects of meteorology are taught. It affords a chance for students to earn a Master of Science degree in meteorology; further study leading to the doctorate is available to highly qualified officers. Finally, the Meteorology Curriculum provides one year of graduate education in meteorology to meet the Navy's basic operational and technical requirements. Enrollment in this curriculum is restricted to graduating students of the Officers Candidate School. Based on their academic performance, officers completing the Meteorology Curriculum have a chance, after one tour in a meteorological billet, to be reassigned to the Postgraduate School where they may work toward a Master of Science degree in meteorology.

Although newly commissioned officers are usually assigned first to a Fleet Weather Central or Facility, other positions are available for subsequent duty. Positions available, for example, are Analyst/Forecaster; Officer in Charge of a Naval Weather Service Environmental Detachment, usually at a Naval Air Station or Naval Station; Shipboard Weather Officer; Research/-Instructor duty; Computer Officer; Staff Meteorologist; Oceanographer; and Flight Meteorologist.

The Navy considers that opportunities for promotion as a Naval Weather Service Officer are excellent. As in any field, the best qualified individuals advance farther and faster. Performance is a key to successful promotion. The current minimum time in rank for promotion to Lieutenant Junior Grade is one year; to Lieutenant, two years; to Lieutenant Commander, four to five years; to Commander, five to six years; and to Captain, five years. In 1970, the basic pay for an Ensign with less than two years' service was about $418 per month, while a Captain with 18 years' service (nearly the minimum time required to reach this grade) earned about $1,425 per month. In addition to basic pay, military personnel receive allowances for quarters and rations, a not inconsiderable addition to their basic salary.

Enlisted weather men in the Navy are called Aerographer's Mates. (An aerographer is a Navy warrant officer who observes and forecasts weather and sea conditions. *Aerology* is the study of the free atmosphere, and until 1957 the term as used in the Navy was synonymous with meteorology; *aerography* is essentially the same as descriptive meteorology.) An Aerographer's Mate may observe, record, collect, and analyze meteorological and oceanographic conditions. He may make visual and instrumental observations; operate a satellite receiver and interpret and apply the data received; plot charts from coded data, operate computer equipment for data processing, analysis, and display; and maintain instrumental equipment. He may also prepare forecasts and warnings of the weather and the state of the sea, and prepare and present briefings on current and forecast weather and sea conditions and their effect on operations. Many of the duties of the Navy's enlisted weather men are implied in the several training programs described below.

Aerographer's Mates are selected by examination from among the Navy's Seamen. In the first three grades, their pay (in 1970) ranged from $232 to $532 per month, the latter after 18 years' service. In the petty officer grades, salaries ranged from $370 to $904 per month after advancement and 26 years' service. Enlisted weather men may achieve the grade of Warrant Officer (Aerographer) or Limited Duty Officer (Meteorologist). Warrant Officers in 1970 earned from $410 to $1054 per month after advancement and 26 years' service. Limited Duty Officers have the same grades and pay as regular officers but are limited to service in their specialty. The salaries quoted are basic pay and are increased significantly by allowances for quarters and rations.

Among the obvious advantages of a career in the Naval Weather Service are the opportunities for education and training. According to the Navy, the things that young officers like best about the Weather Service are the challenge of an important job that is offered to them almost immediately; the *esprit de corps* of the Service; wide recognition by other naval personnel as the "weatherman"; and the chance for advanced study and research. The challenges and trials and tribulations that a Naval Weather Officer can encounter are vividly described in a pamphlet entitled *The Carrier Weather Officer,* publication NWRF 25-0959-025 of the United States Navy Weather Research Facility, U.S. Naval Air Station, Norfolk, Virginia.

For enlisted personnel, aerography is interesting and challenging work in an area that is vital to the Navy's operations. At sea, weather men work above deck; here, as at Naval Air Stations, they have close contact with the men who use the observations they make and the forecasts and warnings they prepare. Since the civilian weather service draws on trained weather men from the Armed Forces to fill jobs in the Meteorological Technician category, training as an Aerographer's Mate may be quite advantageous even for those who do not wish to make a career in the Navy but who leave after their obligated service. Enlisted members of the Naval Weather Service receive training at the Naval Air Training Center at Lakehurst, New Jersey.

At Lakehurst, the 16-week Class (A) School offers the basic

course of study. Students are trained to operate weather facsimile and teletypewriter equipment; to prepare radiosonde transmitters and balloons for release; to perform routine checks and preventive maintenance on nonelectronic equipment; to make, record, and prepare surface and upper-air observations for transmission; to decode, encode, and plot oceanographic and weather data; and to operate satellite reeciving equipment and interpret satellite data. Students also receive a basic course in meteorology and oceanography, including the fundamentals of weather map analysis.

The 24-week Class (B) School provides the advanced study course for petty officers and noncommissioned officers. Trainees are instructed in radar meteorology, satellite meteorology, numerical weather prediction, and the air-ocean environment. They learn to analyze oceanographic, surface, and upper-air charts; to construct prognostic charts and make weather predictions for extended periods and long flights; and to prepare forecasts of wind, waves, and surf. The Class (B) School also includes classes in supervision, familiarization flights in a "Flying Classroom," and field trips to acquaint students with the latest developments in meteorology.

The Class (C) Schools offer shorter, highly specialized courses in upper-air observing techniques and the air-ocean environment.

Ways of getting started in a career as a naval weather officer are described in Chapter 9.

CHAPTER 6

TEACHING AND RESEARCH

METEOROLOGY IN THE UNIVERSITIES

IN 1970, just over 1,000 meteorologists were on the staffs of university departments or programs offering degrees in the atmospheric sciences. These universities, in 1969, granted degrees to some 600 students. However, university-employed meteorologists devoted less than half their time to teaching (Table 3). Research has come to be an important part of the duties of most university science teachers, and this is particularly true of highly active sciences like meteorology. The fact that university staffs in the atmospheric sciences increased threefold during the 1970's is in large part due to a great expansion of government sponsored research in meteorology in that decade. Consulting is also an important activity of university meteorologists.

The opportunities for atmospheric research were greatly enhanced by the nation's space effort in the 1960s and by the vast quantities of new data obtained by satellites and space vehicles. Studies of the very high atmosphere and the atmospheres of other planets became much more feasible, and more teachers and students went into these relatively unexplored fields. A great deal of meteorological research in the lower atmosphere was also stimulated by cloud pictures and radiation data from the TIROS, ESSA, and Nimbus satellites. Research workers immediately began to develop ways of applying the new observations to weather analysis and forecasting. Applications took place probably more rapidly than anyone expected. One of the most notable contributions to the use of satellite data for weather forecasting was made in 1969 by a young meteorologist who did not receive his meteorological training until after the first weather satellite was launched in April 1960.

Recent developments in the application of the satellite to meteorology suggest that there will be a continuing need for teachers to train meteorologists for operational as well as for research jobs in the 1970s. During this decade, the World Weather Program will be developed, the area of practical weather forecasting greatly expanded, and the possibility of useful longer-range forecasts tested. The greater opportunity for obtaining and using weather data should be reflected in an increase in the number of meteorologists employed by the world's weather services and hence in the number of teachers required to train them.

One of the notable developments in the universities during the 1960s was the reorganization of many departments of meteorology along interdisciplinary lines to encourage a unified approach to the study of the physical environment. By this reorganization, meteorologists sound closer ties with the other disciplines of the Earth and space environment. Toward the end of the decade, another trend became apparent as more universities established multidisciplinary programs in environmental health, environmental engineering, and other applied fields. In these programs, meteorology and hydrology occupied a prominent place because of their many applications to the problems of air and water pollution and public health. The actions of the federal government in 1970 in setting up an Environmental Protection Agency and a National Oceanic and Atmospheric Administration were indications that education and research in the environmental sciences would probably continue to receive strong governmental support.

Another development of the 1960s was the growth of Earth science courses in the secondary achools. With the support of the National Science Foundation, an improved Earth science curriculum was developed. Its introduction into the schools set off a demand for many additional well-trained Earth science teachers. By the end of the decade, there was still a strong need for better trained secondary school teachers in this field. State-supported universities with departments offering education majors in Earth science included meteorology as an important part of the curriculum in education. This trend may be expected to continue into the 1970s, for the advent of environmental management as a public issue suggests that courses touching on air and water resources will continue to be popular in the secondary schools for some time to come.

Some authorities believe that a need exists for a semiprofessional corps of meteorological technicians with junior college certificates in meteorology.

The facts cited above can be taken as fairly good evidence that job opportunities will continue to open up in the universities during the 1970s in the areas of teaching and research. In addition to meteorologists trained in the more traditional aspects of the science and its applications, it seems likely that teachers of meteorology and research meteorologists with strong interdisciplinary interests in related sciences and their applications will be in demand: for example, in chemistry and biology as well as in meteorology's traditional fundamental science, physics; in oceanography, hydrology, geochemistry, aeronomy, ecology, and medicine; and in such applied fields as environmental health, air and water pollution, water management, urban design, engineering, and education. Meteorologists have much to contribute to improved understanding leading to better management of the environment.

UNIVERSITY CAREERS

THE DUTIES OF THE UNIVERSITY METEOROLO-GIST may be quite varied, depending upon the requirements of his department and his personal interests. In addition to preparing lectures and meeting his classes, he is probably involved in active research of his own, in overseeing the research of students fulfilling their thesis requirements, or perhaps in supervising research projects undertaken by the university under contracts or grants. He may have to write technical reports on the progress of this research, prepare talks for delivery at scientific meetings and write papers for publication in scientific journals. Meteorology is a highly viable science, with new research continually adding to the body of knowledge, and the university meteorologist must therefore spend much of his time keeping up with newly published results and attending scientific meetings. In addition to pursuing research, he may, during the course of his career, become involved in consulting and working with various agencies and committees of the government, with business and industry, with the scientific and professional societies, and perhaps with semigovernmental bodies like the National Academy of Sciences and the National Academy of Engineering. Frequently, university meteorologists are able to combine private consulting or other work—even weather forecasting for television!—with their university careers.

A graduate student working toward an advanced degree in the atmospheric sciences may serve as an instructor and more frequently as a research assistant. In university meteorology departments, it is quite common for able students to have both research and teaching experience before making a final choice of careers. University teachers are usually classified as instructors, assistant professors, associate professors, and professors. In 1968, the median *academic* year salary of instructors in the atmospheric sciences was $9,700. In 1970, the median salary of assistant professors was $11,400; of associate professors, $13,700; and of full professors, $19,000 for the academic year. On a calendar year basis, teachers' salaries were about 25 percent higher, reflecting their income from other sources.

Although graduate students without advanced degrees frequently work as research assistants, a master's degree is a practical requirement for entering the field of university teaching and research; the present-day requirement for continued advancement is effectively the Ph.D. or Sc.D. This is shown by the fact that in 1968, of those meteorologists with full professorships, 85 percent held doctor's degrees. Continued advancement is an important consideration in a university career, since the right of tenure depends upon promotion within specified time limits. *Tenure,* in effect, guarantees the university professor permanency in the job, preventing dismissal except under very unusual circumstances, and then only through formal proceedings. Some notion of the time required for advancement in a university career may be formed by considering the data on salary versus experience. In 1968, the median salary of university meteorolo-

gists with two to four years' experience was $10,800. Those with
15 to 19 years' experience earned $15,000 a year. Although
meteorology is a relatively small profession, a number of meteorologists have become university deans. Retirement plans are
customary features of university employment. The sabbatical
year—a free year granted for rest, travel, or research—is one of
the very attractive benefits of professorship, as are the traditional
freedom and independence of academic life.

As in other fields, advancement in a university career depends to a very great degree upon one's personal qualifications.
The attributes of the successful teacher and the research scientist
tend to overlap. A love of knowledge, intellectual curiosity,
patience, and enthusiasm appear to be common to both. The
most effective teachers are those who are genuinely excited by
their subject and can, for this reason, convey a sense of its
importance and significance to their students. Meteorology offers
the opportunity for such a sense of excitement because it provides the challenge of great intellectual activity that at the same
time serves humane ideals. For example, as we noted earlier,
meterology has depended historically upon the daily, routine,
worldwide exchange of information founded on countless international conferences and agreements. Meteorology has been
called our single most important bridge to international cooperation.

RESEARCH

IT WAS, IN PART, the global nature of the meteorological
problem that led in the late 1950s to a new organization for
meteorological research, the University Corporation for Atmospheric Research (UCAR). Although most universities with
departments or programs in the atmospheric sciences carry on

research on their own campuses, or at research institutes associated with the universities, by 1970 there were 27 institutions associated with this larger research organization. UCAR, which is funded primarily by the National Science Foundation, operates the National Center for Atmospheric Research (NCAR) at Boulder, Colorado. NCAR was founded in 1960 to provide facilities for atmospheric research on a scale larger than would be feasible at a single university; to serve as a focal point for a vigorous and expanding national program of research in the atmospheric sciences; and to provide a center of intellectual activity that would bring together scientists from meteorology and related physical sciences. The Center's activities have been directed mainly toward the basic understanding of atmospheric phenomena and processes. The Laboratory at Boulder, located atop a mesa at the foot of the Front Range of the Rocky Mountains and one of meteorology's "show places" in the United States, was dedicated in 1967.

NCAR has a visiting scientist program, and its facilities are equally available to scientists from universities and from private and government laboratories in this country and abroad. Its research programs emphasize interdisciplinary problems. In addition to providing joint-use facilities, it manages and participates in large-scale field research programs and supports national and international programs in the atmospheric sciences. In its Annual Report for 1969, the University Corporation identified four long-range objectives:

1. To ascertain the feasibility of controlling weather and climate, to develop the techniques for control, and to bring about the beneficial application of this knowledge;

2. To bring about improved description and prediction

of astrophysical influences on the atmosphere and the space environment of our planet;

3. To bring about improved description and prediction of atmospheric processes and the forecasting of weather and climate;

4. To improve our understanding of the sources of air contamination and to bring about the application of better practices of air conservation.

By the end of its first decade, NCAR had a staff of more than 500 scientists, engineers, technicians, and support people. The scientific staff, which includes about 80 workers at the Ph.D. level, is an interdisciplinary group of meteorologists, physicists, astronomers, mathematicians, chemists, and representatives of other disciplines. Research and operations at NCAR are conducted in the Laboratory of Atmospheric Science, the High Altitude Observatory, the Facilities Laboratory, and the Advanced Study Program. Professional and nonprofessional salaries and other benefits are roughly comparable with those of similar positions in the federal government.

REQUIREMENTS FOR A RESEARCH CAREER

THE DUTIES OF the research meteorologist do not differ greatly between the universities and the government laboratories. Rather, the differences arise in the kind of research being pursued, and this, in turn, depends essentially upon one's qualifications.

The highly gifted research scientist often enjoys the luxury of being able to work on problems of his own choice. While he

The National Hurricane Center is dependent on basic weather data supplied by the National Meteorological Center in Suitland, Md. Here thousands of synoptic reports are received and analyzed daily, mostly by computer. Weather observations taken at sea are an important input.

may rely on computer programers and other researchers for support, his work is, by its very nature, largely his own creation. Because there is a community of aims and of recognized problems, an individual's contribution may set other scientists working along the same line. With organized support from government, and the missions of the various agencies tending to control much research, much of the scientific effort involves groups of meteorologists rather than the lone worker. The extensive observational programs and the large computers often required for research have intensified this trend. However, the recognition and solution of fundamental problems requiring great intellectual effort and insight still remain the function of one or a few gifted individuals in their various fields. These scientists quite often have a group of "pupils" or coworkers, both at the universities and in the research laboratories, who are guided by and learn from them.

Frequently, the answers to basic questions depend on the solutions to many lesser problems. These can often be solved in a straightforward way by gathering and analyzing data and drawing conclusions. Much research of this kind has to be done. Since it can be rather clearly defined, it is often contracted for and accomplished by research firms, institutes, and universities. Sometimes a large data-gathering effort, perhaps involving special observing stations, instruments, airplanes, balloons, and other equipment may be called for. Such field experiments may be cooperative ventures involving the universities, the National Center for Atmospheric Research, the National Oceanic and Atmospheric Administration, the Naval Weather Service, and the Air Weather Service. Quite often, specialized instruments have to be developed to answer specific questions.

Because research in meteorology, and the support of such research, involves such varied activities, many kinds of individuals with many different kinds of skills, talents, interests, and experience can find careers in the field. High intellectual ability, imagination, inventiveness, practicality, management ability, and an adventurous spirit are all needed, but obviously not in the same individual.

In 1970, 450 scientists named the management and administration of atmospheric research as their primary work. Since meterology is so largely a responsibility of the federal government, most such research in the United States is government supported. New directions in the science may come initially from one or more of the committees of the National Academy of Science or the National Academy of Engineering. Long-range plans are developed by the Federal Coordinator for Meteorology, in the National Oceanic and Atmospheric Administration.

In 1970, the median annual salary of atmospheric scientists engaged primarily in research was $15,600, compared with an average for the field of $15,200. Managers of research received the highest median salary in the atmospheric sciences, $20,400 per year.

CONSULTING

AS WE HAVE POINTED OUT, university employment often lends itself to the private practice of consulting. Meteorological consulting has come about partly as the result of the need on the part of business, industry, and agriculture for specialized services that are not considered to be the responsibility of the federal government. Government agencies, also, frequently have to go outside the official meteorological organizations for advice, just as they go to the universities for research talent. Consulting is discussed further in the following chapter.

TABLE 3

*Primary Duties of Atmospheric and Space Scientists
Employed by Universities and Colleges in 1968*

Activity	Number employed
Research and development	407
Basic research	285
Applied research	122
Teaching	225
Management or administration	60
Administration of research	39
Other activity or no report	65
Total	757

CHAPTER 7

METEOROLOGY IN BUSINESS AND INDUSTRY

IN THE UNITED STATES, before the advent of commercial aviation, the practice of meteorology as a profession was confined almost completely to the civilian and military services of the federal government. A few meteorologists taught at universities, but meteorology was essentially a government monopoly. However, beginning in the 1920s and 1930s, some of the newly established commercial airlines found it necessary to set up their own weather forecasting offices to provide their pilots with the specialized weather information they had to have for their operations. After World War II, the private practice of meteorology was considerably broadened when many war-trained weather officers returning to civilian life saw possibilities for work outside the government services and the airlines. The war had spurred research, and some of these new civilian meteorologists organized departments of meteorology at a number of universities, supplementing the five or six then in existence. Others saw opportunities in radio and, a few years later, in television weather broadcasting. Still others, after the early experiments in cloud seeding in the 1940s, went into "commercial rainmaking," contracting with groups of farmers and with municipalities and utility companies to attempt to increase rainfall or snowfall. A number of public utilities, atomic and nuclear energy installations, insurance companies, and other businesses were soon providing further opportunities for the private practice of meteorology, either by employing meteorologists or contracting with the new consulting firms that were beginning to spring up.

Excluding the university meteorologists engaged in consulting, there are now more than 800 professional scientists who practice meteorology as a business or who work for business or industrial concerns. During the 1960s, the percentage of meteorologists working in business and industry showed an upward trend, while the percentage employed by the government services decreased slightly. (The actual *numbers* employed in all categories increased, of course, as the proportionate number in each category fell or rose.)

Meteorology apart from government and the universities can be practiced in several ways. First of all, a meteorologist may be self-employed, pursuing a professional career individually, just as some other engineering and industrial consultants do. Frequently, meteorologists having part-time or full-time employment—as in the case of university meteorologists (Chapter 6)—practice consulting as a means of supplementing their income. Several meteorologists may also associate in a company or firm organized specifically for the practice of meteorology. In another category, a meteorologist may work as a permanent employee of a business or industrial corporation where his duties are devoted either in part or wholly to weather or weather-related problems, depending on the company's needs. Finally, the meteorologist may be a member of a group employed by a corporation with specialized, full-time meteorological activities, such as an airline with its own meteorological service or a large business or consulting firm in which meteorology is only one of a number of diversified services.

AIRLINE METEOROLOGY

THE SEVERAL HUNDRED METEOROLOGISTS employed by the airlines form the largest single group in business and industry. An airline meteorology department may consist of groups of forecasters working at several key dispatch locations. Using the basic weather observations, analyses, and forecasts prepared by the National Weather Service and available from teletypewriter and facsimile "drops," the airline meteorologist prepares weather forecasts and briefings tailored to his airline's special needs. Among these are the enroute temperature and wind forecasts, selection of the most economical and comfortable flight path, identification of areas of turbulence, etc. The efficiency of jet engines depends fairly critically on temperature or air density; and head or tail winds over a long distance can mean large variations in the fuel needed and in the time of the flight. By selecting the smoothest route, airline meteorologists can assure the company's passengers a comfortable ride. In recent years, airline research meteorologists have investigated ways of detecting clear air turbulence, techniques of removing fog at airports, and other aviation weather problems. In addition to providing weather support for their own airline operations, some airline meteorology departments offer consulting, research, forecasting, and other services to outside users.

METEOROLOGICAL CONSULTING FIRMS

ABOUT FIFTY meteorological consulting firms advertise their services in the Professional Directory of the *Bulletin of the American Meteorological Society*. Consulting and research are the services most frequently advertised by these firms, with forecasting services a close third. Some supply forecasts for private and "executive" aircraft flights, a much-needed service, since statistics show that aircraft accidents resulting from adverse weather are most frequent among noncommercial aircraft. Ship routing is another forecasting service offered by some consulting firms, and supplying weather services for television broadcasting is another. Since it has been shown to be economically advantageous to disperse certain types of fog from airports for landing and takeoff, fog dispersal is now a leading commercial application of the weather modification services provided by other firms (Chapters 2 and 5). Still others supply meteorological instrumentation for aircraft and other applications. Some offer air pollution surveys, of obvious value to industries and to government authorities in planning the best locations for factories, refineries, mills, and power plants. The preparation of forecasts and climatological studies for marketing products is another activity of the consultant. The service best known to the general public is television weathercasting.

WEATHER BROADCASTING

SOME METEOROLOGISTS who began their TV weather careers when public television was in its infancy still have programs on the air. Most have combined weathercasting with their own consulting businesses, with teaching, or with other employment. Some follow the National Weather Service's official forecast, supplementing this with weather maps and explaining the anticipated weather developments, air circulation, and movements of weather systems like highs, lows, fronts, lines of thunderstorms, and cloud and rain areas. Others prefer to use their own forecasts, on the ground that weather forecasting is still an individual skill in spite of the great advances in numerical forecasting. They note, too, that the TV forecaster must answer personally to his audience for the accuracy of his forecasts. As one TV meteorologist put it, "Private meteorology is a difficult field, characterized by psychological pressures. But it makes life interesting!"

As the private practice of meteorology gained momentum after World War II, some confusion inevitably arose over the respective roles of the private sector meteorologist and the Weather Bureau's public service weather men. Most problems of this kind have been resolved. The weather observations, analyses, maps, and forecasts of the National Weather Service are available on an immediate basis to the private meteorologist, who simply pays for the teletypewriter and facsimile drops on the circuits needed to supply his office with the necessary basic weather information to conduct a forecast service. (See Chapter 4.) With the rapid growth of meteorology and weather observing and computing technologies, many government meteorologists were needed for the expanding technical and operational work in the national weather services, such as that carried on in the National Meteorological Center and the National Environmental Satellite Service. Many Weather Bureau offices that had served the general public in downtown locations moved to airports. The close contact that had existed between the Weather Bureau and the public for many years was partially severed simply because of changing technologies and an expanding public. The telephone forecast and the TV weather man have filled this gap to some extent. Much more weather information is avilable today than ever before, yet much of it is not freely available to the general public on demand. With increased travel and recreation and a highly mobile public, one cannot avoid the feeling that an opportunity exists for the private meteorologist who can offer specific weather advice to the individual who has specific questions—a service that the impersonal broadcast of weather information does not offer.

INDUSTRIAL METEOROLOGY

WHILE TELEVISION offers good opportunities to some private meteorologists, many others have found their best clients among the more specialized users of weather data. Gas and electric companies must have accurate temperature forecasts, both winter and summer, to plan for dispatching gas and electricity. If more electricity is used than is immediately available, power failures occur. Temperature differences of only a few degrees can be critical. Insurance companies must know how to assign weather risks. Although nearly every industry in the country has some economic stake in the weather, insurance companies measure their liability to weather damage in terms of billions of dollars. Their annual losses from hurricanes, tornadoes, hailstorms, combinations of hail and wind, and other intense storms amount to hundreds of millions of dollars annually. Various kinds of problems must be solved by meteorologists who either consult for or work for insurance companies.

Suppose, for example, that an insurance company has had a series of years with heavy losses in a particular area of the country. Can the same losses be expected in the future, or were the losses due to an abnormal run of weather situations? Because the reduction of injuries and damage caused by or related to weather is very much in an insurance company's interest, one large company has operated a large meteorological research center (disbanded, however, in 1970), and it continues to run a public weather service. Making road and weather conditions continually known to the public, especially during dangerous driving conditions, can be a service that benefits both the insurance industry and the general public.

Besides the utilities, there are other industries in which meteorological advice is essential. For example, nuclear energy plants must be sited, designed, and operated with expert meteorological advice at hand because the hazard of accidental or planned release of radioactive materials is directly related to weather conditions. The aircraft industry, in planning new aircraft, must have specializd advice from the meteorologist, as well as the aeronautical engineer who designs the planes, to anticipate what kind of gust loads the plane may experience. An oil-producing company drilling offshore must know the best time to move its rig to another location when the well is finished. What risks are encountered in towing the rig, and how are these related to season? If a severe storm occurred during the tow, the disaster might well be complete. A beet grower is paid by the sugar content of his crop, which depends on the stage of development at which the crop is harvested. If the weather is good for harvesting, shall the grower go ahead even though the beets will yield 15 per cent less sugar than if he waits? If he waits, what are the chances of a heavy rain making the fields impassable?

The foregoing are only a few examples of the ways in which private meteorologists can apply their knowledge. The applications of meteorological information to business and industry are indeed endless. To the misfortune of our industrialized society, they are often unexploited [1]. The blight of air pollution is one that can be ameliorated by the proper location of power plants, mills, and factories with due regard to the local climate and topography and the advice of a competent expert in atmospheric pollution. The increase in the evolution of mine gas and of fatal mine explosions with a sharp fall in barometric pressure is well documented, but nothing is being done in the United States, at this writing (1970), to apply such information.

CERTIFICATES AND SEALS OF APPROVAL

WITH THE RAPID GROWTH of the private practice of meteorology in the 1950s, it became clear that the professional and scientific integrity of meteorology would be safeguarded by a certification program, which the American Meteorological Society undertook to establish (Chapter 10). The Society considers the essential attribute of the consultant to be "a specialized knowledge combined with a broad background, an ingrained concept of service, and a clear and unwavering recognition of the importance of the rules for professional conduct." He is a practicing professional whose work is based on a good understanding of the existing knowledge of the atmosphere and its behavior, and on the ability he has acquired in applying this understanding to the vital affairs of men. The meteorological consultant may make his services available, on an individual basis, to a great many clients on a fee-for-services-rendered plan, or, alternatively, he may work for a single company or government agency for a salary instead of a fee. By 1970, about 100 meteorologists had been certified as consulting meteorologists by the American Meteorological Society.

To receive certification, the applicant must be a professional member of the Society; be a graduate of a university or college with successful completion of professional courses in meteorology of a satisfactory standard; pass an oral and a written examination prepared by the Society's Board of Certified Consulting Meteorologists; have a minimum professional experience of five years; and possess traits of character giving assurance that he will observe the rules of professional ethics set by the Society (Chapter 10).

Radio and television weathercasting is another area in which it was found advisable to set standards, since some of the earlier nonprofessional performers often presented the weather forecast under the guise of entertainment rather than information. In 1957, the American Meteorological Society set up a plan to grant Seals of Approval for professional members of the Society who have radio and television weather programs that meet set standards. The applicant's qualifications and his programs are carefully reviewed by professional meteorologists in the broadcast area, and by the Society's Board of Radio and Television Weathercasting. The Board's evaluation is based on the informational value of the program, audience interest, educational value, and the performer's professional attitude. Since the beginning of this program, the Society has granted Seals of Approval to 42 radio and 77 television weather broadcasters. These figures give an indication of the number of professional meteorologists engaged in weather broadcasting.

CAREER REQUIREMENTS

THE SELF-EMPLOYED METEOROLOGIST, or the meteorologist who heads a consulting firm, should be fairly well established in his profession. He has to be self-reliant and resourceful, and able to combine salesmanship and an aptitude for business with sound scientific and technical knowledge and experience. In general, the skill of the industrial or business meteorologist is measured by the amount of money saved or damage avoided and sometimes by lives saved. As in any business, the private meteorologist must convince his employer or his client that the cost of his services is exceeded by the benefits gained.

In 1970, the median annual salary of the 102 meteorologists who named consulting as their primary work activity was $16,200. The median salary of self-employed meteorologists was $17,500, the highest in the profession.

REFERENCES

1. Myers, Joel N., and John J. Cahir. "The Weather Business," *Weatherwise.* Vol. 24, No. 2, April 1971, p. 64.

CHAPTER 8

EMPLOYMENT OUTLOOK, SALARIES, AND BENEFITS

METEOROLOGISTS PRESENTLY MAKE UP only about two percent of all American physical and social scientists, and job openings are of the order of 500 or 600 per year. This is not a large number compared with such professions as engineering, for example. Since about 80 percent of U.S. meteorologists are either directly employed by the federal government or are supported to some extent by federal funds, employment is closely related to government policies—to a much greater extent than in other sciences except in areas that rely wholly on government contracts. The fact that most meteorologists are employed by the government gives some measure of stability to employment in meteorology, for, in the government, reductions in the work force are ordinarily managed through attrition; that is, by reducing the numbers of positions when employees retire or change jobs. However, the actual number of meteorologists employed from year to year fluctuates with government plans, programs, and spending. Broadly speaking, for the reasons mentioned in Chapter 1, meteorology is still largely a government "monopoly."

Although in 1970 and early 1971 employment opportunities in meteorology were somewhat less numerous than in earlier years—reflecting a slight economic recession and a leveling off of government expenditures for science—there were sound reasons for believing that the demand for professional meteorologists would continue to expand during the 1970s. According to the 1970-71 edition of the Department of Labor's *Occupational Outlook Handbook* [1], several factors were expected to maintain employment opportunities for graduates in meteorology or atmospheric science. Among these were the normal growth of the profession, the increase in college enrollments, advances in meteorological technology, and wider demands for meteorological services.

Salaries of meteorologists are generally competitive with those in other sciences, and reflect to a considerable extent the pay scales in the civil and military services of the government. This may be because qualified applicants are relatively few and competition for their services is largely between the federal government and the universities, where much of the research and teaching are directly or indirectly supported by government. The salaries quoted in this book are, with a few exceptions, those from a 1970 survey of U.S. scientists [3]. In 1970, the federal government completed a three-year period of salary adjustment for its employees, at the close of which salaries were to be comparable with those in business and industry for similar kinds of work and responsibility. In 1971, Congress authorized the Executive Branch of the government to make salary adjustments for most of its employees.

For most meteorologists, benefits apart from salary include vacation and sick leave, health and life insurance, and retirement

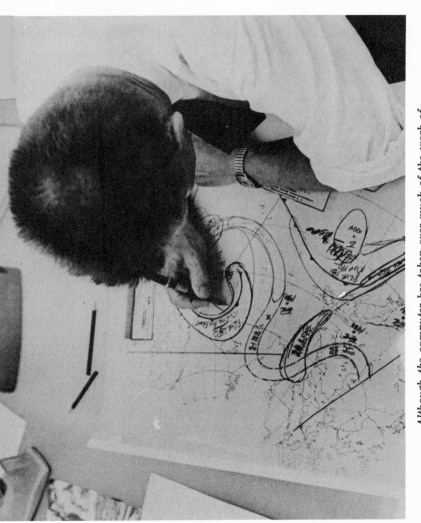

Although the computer has taken over much of the work of preparing charts, many are still hand-produced. These also serve as backups in case of power or computer failure.
Courtesy of ESSA

annuities. For most, these are the benefits provided in the career service of the federal government, the Armed Forces, the universities, and the commercial air lines.

EMPLOYMENT PROSPECTS

ACCORDING TO THE DEPARTMENT OF LABOR [1], the demand for meteorologists should continue good throughout the 1970s. In Chapter 2, we have seen that our modern society, both on the national and international scenes, should require more and more meteorological services. Advances in observing techniques, in computers, and in the science itself have brought meteorology to a revolutionary stage of development. The increasing "know-how" of meteorologists should itself create new opportunities for employment. Public concern over the quality of the environment should result in the creation of new jobs, both in the public and private sectors of meteorology, as demands increase for more detailed monitoring of the atmosphere, better siting of power plants and other industrial installations, more effective planning of cities, and better applications of environmental health and engineering knowledge in our society.

Opportunities to study the weather on a global scale will be particularly good for meteorologists trained in processing, analyzing, and interpreting data obtained by spacecraft and weather satellites, as the World Weather Program develops during the 1970's. Observations from satellites are continually offering new data for research and operational uses. Meteorologists, especially those with advanced degrees, will be needed to conduct research in the colleges and universities. As college enrollments rise and the number of university departments granting degrees in atmospheric science increases, the number of teaching positions will also increase. Between 1968 and 1970, nine additional departments of atmospheric science were established in universities, an increase of 20 percent in two years. Recent statistics [3] show that the number of meteorologists at universities tripled during the late 1960s, perhaps as government policies resulted in the diversion of research from government agencies to the universities. The need of civil and military weather services for trained meteorologists to translate computer-processed weather data into usable forecasts for the general public and for aviation, marine, and other users of weather information apparently also is increasing the demand for university meteorologists to train newcomers to the field. As the contributions that meteorology can make to other scientific and engineering fields become increasingly evident—as, for example, in the burgeoning field of environmental management—it is probable that numerous multidisciplinary programs involving atmospheric science will be created in the universities.

During the 1970s, there should also be a demand for meteorologists to develop and improve instruments such as radar and radio probes, lidar, high altitude balloons, and the measuring or sensing devices of rockets and satellites—all aimed at increasing the density of weather observations over the globe. Long-established research programs concerned with the investigation of severe local storms, such as tornadoes, thunderstorms, and squall lines, and of larger storms, like hurricanes and winter snow storms, will offer continuing opportunities. Research on turbulence—for example, the clear-air turbulelnce that high-flying aircraft encounter without warning, and boundary-layer turbulence near the Earth's surface—and on air-sea interactions, will impose a continuing requirement for meteorologists. Air pollution research is of particular importance because of the serious pollution problems besetting our rapidly growing urban areas.

During the late 1960s, the general public became more acutely aware of the serious health hazards of air pollution, which biometeorologists had been pointing out for some decades. In 1970, the President and Congress responded to this public concern with the National Environmental Policy Act of 1969 and the establishment of the President's Council on Environmental Quality. Thus, better management of the environment, including the vital resources of the atmosphere, became a stated national policy. In July 1970, the President announced a reorganization plan that drew together in a proposed new Environmental Protection Agency those functions of government concerned with the quality of the environment and environmental health. The new agency, organized later in the year, absorbed the National Air Pollution Control Administration, formerly in the Department of Health, Education, and Welfare, as well as other units of the federal government concerned with environmental research, monitoring, standards-setting, and enforcement activities. As a result of these developments, the functions of government were broadened, and it seemed probable that new opportunities in the field of environmental engineering would open up during the decade of the seventies. It was anticipated that meteorologists with supplementary training in atmospheric chemistry, environmental health science, urban planning, and similar disciplines would be needed to fill new jobs in local and state agencies involved in monitoring air quality and in establishing and maintaining standards. It was expected also that industry and industrial consulting firms would find new needs for meteorologists specializing in air pollution and engineering problems, such as the siting of power plants and other facilities.

There should, of course, be a continuing need for meteorologists to work in the existing operational programs that supply the country's basic and specialized weather services—primarily in the National Weather Service, the Air Weather Service, the Naval Weather Service, the commercial airlines, and some of the utilities. As more planes are placed in service, more meteorologists will be required to assist in determining the safest and smoothest in-flight routes. The commercial airlines and the National Weather Service will require forecasters, briefers, and radar observers to meet continuing demands for aviation weather service as newer types of commercial aircraft come into greater use—helicopters, "executive" aircraft, and supersonic aircraft, for example. Marine weather forecasts for recreational boating and for oceanographic operations will probably become more highly specialized during the coming decade and will require additional meteorologists. Weather forecasters and aeronomists will be needed to support the nation's space effort—to supply forecasts at launching and splashdown and to predict streams of solar radiation that might constitute a hazard for our astronauts, as well as to study the atmospheres of other planets.

Recognition by business and industry of the economic value of weather forecasts, short of the "perfect" forecast that may very well never be attained, also should create additional jobs in applied meteorology. As skill in long-range weather forecasting increases—as it probaby will under the impetus of the World Weather Program—more meteorologists should find openings in industrial concerns, shipping companies, and other business ventures. The private practice of meteorology should offer increasing opportunities.

Opportunities for civilian meteorologists in the Armed Forces are not expected to increase significantly during the 1970s. There should, however, be a need for military meteorologists to replace those leaving the services, as there will be for retiring meteorologists in the civil arm of the government.

The probable need for professional meteorologists to replace those retiring during the 1970s is illustrated graphically in Figure 1. The graph shows how the age distribution of professional meteorologists compared, in 1970, with that of all scientists registered. About 35 percent of all employed meteorologists were 45 years old, or older, in that year. With increasingly liberal retirement benefits, it was expected that many of these employees would retire during the coming decade, and that between 200 and 300 meteorologists would be needed each year simply as replacements for the retirees. A large number of these older meteorologists are employed in NOAA and other civilian agencies, where retirement with full benefits is optional at age 55 after 30 years' service. Thus, an increasing demand for meteorologists to fill vacancies in the civil service should begin early in the 1970s and continue for several years, peaking around 1975.

Table 4, page 153, abstracted from the National Register [3], shows where *atmospheric and space scientists* (essentially the same group designated as *meteorologists* in earlier surveys) were employed in 1970. During the late 1960s, personnel ceilings imposed on some agencies had evidently limited the employment of meteorologists in the federal government to those required for the replacement of personnel retiring or resigning, and employment declined slightly in the military weather services. However, the percental increase in meteorologists employed by educational institutions during the sixties was particularly large. As we have indicated, priorities created by the Vietnam war, national policy with respect to the conduct of research supported by the federal government, and federal budgets as authorized by Congress were all influencing the employment of meteorologists in 1970. Future government policies and spending would determine where the job openings in meteorology would occur for the most part—whether in the civil agencies of the government, the military weather services, or the universities—and, to some extent, in private industry.

National concern about environmental pollution is expected to result in more jobs for meteorologists in the civil agencies of both federal and state governments, as well as some local governments, and perhaps to create a demand for private meteorological consultants, as well.

SALARIES

TABLE 4, in addition to employment figures, shows the median salaries paid to atmospheric and space scientists in 1970 [3]. For all civilian meteorologists (atmospheric and space scientists in the survey), the median salary was $15,200, a figure slightly higher than the median for scientists in all fields. Ninety percent of the meteorologists surveyed earned more than $10,000 per year, and about ten percent earned more than $22,300 per year. After the latest pay adjustment in January 1971, meteorologists with a bachelor's degree could expect to enter the federal government service at a salary of $8,324 or $10,298, depending on their college records. Meteorologists who had completed all requirements for the master's degree, or those having two years of graduate work, could start at $11,517 or $12,615, while those with the Ph.D. degree could begin at $12,615 or $15,040, depending on qualifications.

Among the large body of meteorologists, education is a better index of salary than one's place of employment. The salaries of meteorologists at educational institutions are somewhat lower than the median value; however, it should be remembered that this group includes a large number of students and younger individuals, and that university scientists often have the opportunity to increase their income through consulting fees. On the whole, the salaries of professional meteorologists having similar education tend to be about the same among different employers. In 1970, the average civilian meteorologist with a Ph.D. degree earned a salary of about $17,600; one with a master's degree, about $15,800; and one with a bachelor's degree, about $15,000. Civilian meteorologists with less education than the bachelor's degree were paid a median salary of about $14,000 a year. Meteorologists with a doctorate degree could command unusually high salaries in business and industry, the median (in 1968) being $21,600.

We have pointed out earlier that American meteorologists work at many points within the United States and around the world. National Weather Service meteorologists working abroad are confined mainly to countries in which the United States has territorial rights, and to the Arctic and Antarctic regions. Cost-of-living allowances and pay differentials, and, in some cases, post exchange and commissary privileges, sometimes make these posts attractive to applicants having an adventurous spirit—or to those who simply wish to save money in an area where it may not be practicable to spend it!

For a variety of reasons, the median salaries of meteorologists differ somewhat, depending on the location of the job. Table 5 shows the number of professional meteorologists working in states where more than 100 were employed, with the exception of Alaska. In general, the highest salaries are paid in areas where there are large numbers of meteorologists employed in managerial or highly technical jobs (the Washington, D.C., metropolitan area) or areas in which research and development activities are concentrated (Massachusetts, California, and Colorado).

OTHER BENEFITS

IN ADDITION TO their salaries, most meteorologists receive so-called "fringe benefits" that can be considered part of the compensation they receive from their employers. About a third of those presently employed (1970) receive the customary benefits of U.S. Civil Service employment: a rather liberal retirement plan; vacation leave of 13 to 26 days each year depending on length of service; 13 days of paid sick leave annually; optional participation in low-cost group life and health insurance programs supported in part by the government; and unusually good opportunities for professional training at universities (Chapter 3) as well as other training within the agency.

Meteorologists who make a career in the Armed Forces receive the same benefits as other military personnel, including retirement after 20 years at half pay, insurance, medical care, training, and the opportunity of buying at post exchanges and commissaries. Each year, the U.S. Air Force selects about 200 new college graduates who have received Air Force commissions and sends them to universities for training. Servicemen with such training are highly qualified for positions as civilian meteorologists if they decide against a military career after their periods of enlistment.

Meteorologists employed at universities or in private industry and business receive, in general, the same benefits as other employees in these fields. Traditional university fringe benefits are those of *tenure*—the practice under which a professor may be assured of permanent employment after a trial period of several years—and the *sabbatical*—a periodic year of leave from assigned duties often used for travel, study, or research.

WOMEN IN METEOROLOGY

IF CURRENT STATISTICS are a useful guide, the outlook for women meteorologists is somewhat less bright than for other women scientists. (Most women scientists are concentrated in the fields of chemistry, psychology, biological sciences, and mathematics.) However, in 1970 the National Register counted 102 women professional meteorologists. A number of these have achieved prominence in the fields of research, teaching, writing, and management. Indeed, since less than two percent of the professional meteorologists are women, female students might regard meteorology as a potentially challenging profession! It is true that the rotating shifts required of many operational and service meteorologists are not particularly attractive to women with family responsibilities, but a small number of women have found congenial jobs in operational and service jobs as well as in research and teaching. Several women meteorologists are in charge of National Weather Service field offices.

REFERENCES

1. U.S. Department of Labor. *Occupational Outlook Handbook.* 1970-1971 Edition. Washington, D.C.: U.S. Government Printing Office.

2. National Science Foundation. *American Science Manpower 1968, A Report of the National Register of Scientific and Technical Personnel.* Washington, D.C.: U.S. Government Printing Office.

3. National Science Foundation. "Salaries and Selected Characteristics of U.S. Scientists, 1970," *Reviews of Data on Science Resources,* No. 19, December, 1970.

TABLE 4

Number of Atmospheric and Space Scientists According to Employer and Median Annual Salary, 1970

Employer	Number of Scientists	Median Salary
Educational Institutions	1,017	$13,500 (Academic year)
		14,500 (Calendar year)
Federal government	2,053	15,600
Other government	118	13,200
Military	2,131	———
Nonprofit organizations	96	15,600
Industry and business	768	15,000
Self-employed	45	17,500
Other	16	———
Not employed	341	———
Seeking employment	108	———
Not seeking employment	120	———
Retired	113	———
No report	52	———
Total	6,637	15,200

TABLE 5

Job Locations of Atmospheric and Space Scientists, 1970

Location	Number Employed	Location	Number Employed
California	741	New York	367
Colorado	256	Ohio	103
District of		Pennsylvania	151
Columbia	254	Texas	307
Florida	293	Virginia	182
Illinois	325	Washington	172
Maryland	467	Other contiguous states	47*
Massachusetts	295	Alaska	72
Michigan	105	Hawaii	120
Missouri	119	Canal Zone, Puerto	
Nebraska	144	Rico, and Guam	70
New Jersey	111	Foreign countries	475

---

*Average of individual states

FIGURE 1

Age Distribution of Professional Meteorologists (Atmospheric and Space Scientists) Compared with Other Scientists, 1970

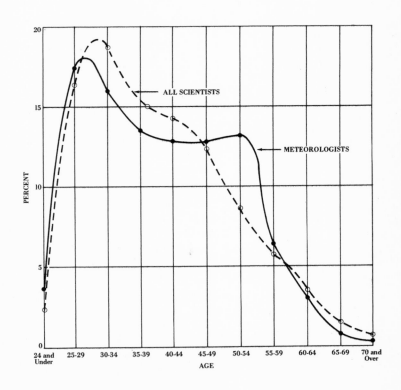

CHAPTER 9

GETTING STARTED

METEOROLOGY IS still a relatively small, though expanding field. For this reason, the student of meteorology will usually, by the time he is ready to apply for a job, have fairly clear and well-defined ideas about getting employment. Let us recall briefly the major areas of employment open to him: the U.S. Civil Service, the Armed Forces, the universities, the airlines, meteorological consulting firms, and some business and industrial concerns. Before he receives his degree, the student may already have committed himself, through one of the Reserve Officers Training Corps programs, to a period of service as a weather officer in the Air Force or Navy (Chapter 5). He may have made arrangements with the head of his university department of meteorology to continue at the university as a research assistant and/or instructor (Chapter 6). He may already have arranged for a job through the personnel officer of one of the government agencies, an aerospace firm, or other large industrial research organization, who make recruiting trips annually to the universities.

If he has a student membership in the American Meteorological Society, the student may receive for a nominal fee a monthly announcement of job openings in all employment fields except the federal government (Chapter 10). He will also find advertisements of job openings in the geophysical sciences in the news magazines of several other professional societies (Chapter 10). These magazines include *EoS, Geotimes,* and *Science.* The Association of American Geographers (1146 16th St., N.W., Washington, D.C. 20036) publishes *Jobs in Geography,* a monthly listing of openings that frequently require specialties in meteorology and climatology.

JOBS IN CIVIL SERVICE

STUDENTS AND OTHER INDIVIDUALS interested in a meteorological career in the U.S. Civil Service apply by filling out a U.S. Civil Service form, SF 171, and submitting it to the personnel officer of the government agency in which they are interested, or to the Civil Service Commission. If you are interested, for example, in employment in the National Oceanic and Atmospheric Administration, you should direct your letter with the accompanying SF 171 to Chief, Personnel, at this agency in Rockville, Maryland 20852. Standard Form 171 requires information on education, experience, and other personal data relevant to employment. Blank forms are available at local post offices.

Although all the information needed to determine whether you are qualified for a particular job must appear on the application form (SF 171), the officials who actually fill positions from among available applicants often find an accompanying letter of application helpful in determining whether to request a personal interview. When a vacancy occurs, the personnel office obtains the files of qualified applicants from the Civil Service Commission and supplies these to the appointing officer or officers. The latter examine all the files, choose qualified candidates, and rate these according to their qualifications. If you feel that because of your university standing, your thesis, research, or other experience you are particularly well qualified in some area, then you should certainly bring out this information in your letter accompanying the standard form. The form should be filled in carefully and the letter well composed.

It is possible that as a meteorology student or science-fair finalist you worked in a summer job in NOAA or some other federal agency (Chapter 3). Although Civil Service positions are filled under the competitive procedure described above (or by actual examination in other areas), summer employment provides actual work experience as well as your supervisor's appraisal, both of which are pertinent in the selection of an applicant. Summer examinations for high school seniors and undergraduate students are usually announced in November of each year.

The meteorological technician jobs in Civil Service are, to a great extent, currently filled by applicants leaving the Armed Forces. These individuals are well trained, experienced in weather observing and similar duties, and often are well qualified in other respects.

THE MILITARY SERVICES

FOR THE STUDENT who must fulfill his military service obligations and who also requires financial assistance with his education, the Air Force Reserve Officers Training Corps (AFROTC), and the Naval Officers Reserve Officers Training Corps (NROTC) offer ways of getting started on a career in meteorology. Details of the various ways of entering military weather careers are described below at some length, since military meteorologists comprise one-third of the profession. Information may be obtained from your university ROTC program. Additional information about careers in the Air Weather Service may be obtained from the Department of the Air Force, Headquarters Air Weather Service (MAC), Scott Air Force Base, Illinois 62225; and about careers in the Naval Weather Service, from the Naval Weather Service Command, Building 200, Washington Navy Yard, Washington, D.C. 20390.

AFROTC Program

Students attending a college or university under an AFROTC program must successfully complete the first two years of the program. They may then apply for meteorology in advanced AFROTC; to be eligible, they must (1) be pursuing an accredited meteorology program or (2) be planning to take college mathematics through calculus and six semester hours of college physics. Upon graduation from AFROTC, the student is commissioned a second lieutenant in the U.S. Air Force Reserve and is called to duty for four years. Students who have taken a meteorology program in college may be assigned directly to duty as a weather officer. Those who have not taken the meteorology program but are selected for AWS will be assigned as second lieutenant to a civilian university for a nine-to-twelve month program in meteorology. After completion of the program, the latter are assigned to an AWS unit for three years' service as a weather officer.

Civil Reservist Plan

Participants in this plan come from two sources: personnel with prior service and individuals being released from active duty and assigned to the reserve program. The plan is available only to those who hold a commission in the USAF Reserve, and is designed to provide additional officers and airmen who would be needed by AWS in the event of war or national emergency. Advantages of active participation in the program are pay, promotion and retirement benefits, reserve assignments near home, choice of training categories, and use of base exchange, commissary, open mess, base theater, and under certain circumstances, hospital care.

Enlisted Air Force Weather Men

Career weather airmen are selected from enlisted airmen who have better than average scores on the Air Force qualifying tests. High school courses in algebra, plane and solid geometry, trigonometry, general science, physics, and chemistry are helpful in qualifying for technical training. Airmen selected for technical training attend a weather course at Chanute Air Force Base, Rantoul, Illinois. Trainees take a 17-week course in observing and reporting weather, or, if qualified, a 33-week course in maintaining weather equipment. These courses enable the career weather airman to progress to supervisory levels in either weather observing or instrument maintenance. The airmen observers may qualify later for forecasting duty.

Airman Commissioning Program

An airman interested in becoming a career weather officer can do so through the Airman Commissioning Program, which provides undergraduate meteorological education followed by officer training and commissioning as an Air Force weather officer. The applicants for this program are carefully screened. The program is conducted in two phases, academic and military.

Normally, the academic phase does not exceed 24 consecutive months. After completing this part of the program, the individual begins military training at the Officer Training School, Lackland AFB, Texas, leading to a commission.

To be eligible for the Airman Commissioning Program, the applicant must have at least one year of active duty, possess those qualities desired in a commissioned officer, and must have completed at least 30 semester-hours or 45 quarter-hours of transferable college credits (grades of C or better). Airmen selected are sent to a civilian college or university at Air Force expense to earn a degree. Airmen who already have completed four years of college and have been accepted for OTS go directly to Lackland AFB for officer training. Following commissioning as a second lieutenant in the Air Force Reserve, officers are assigned to active duty in weather work for a minimum of four years. Weather officers who have completed this program are also eligible for graduate training in meteorology at a later date.

Naval Weather Officers

The Naval Weather Service obtains its officers in ways closely paralleling those of the Air Weather Service. The Officer Candidate School, which is designed for the college graduate, is a primary source of Naval weather officers. Weather officers are also drawn from the Reserve Officer Training Corps, from the U.S. Naval Academy, from other categories of the military services, and by promotion from the enlisted ranks. Applications to the Officer Training School may be made through Navy Recruiting Stations. To insure assignment in a meteorology position, the applicant should make certain that he indicates his wish to be designated an "1815 officer," since this four-digit code identifies a Meteorology Officer.

Aerographer's Mates

Enlisted weather men in the Navy are selected from among the Navy's Seamen. As in the Air Weather Service, enlisted men may advance to the officer grades by fulfilling educational requirements to become Limited Duty Officers (Chapter 5).

THE PRIVATE SECTOR

GETTING STARTED on a meteorological career in the Civil or Military Services is a relatively standardized procedure. This is not true, in general, in the private sector of meteorology. Here, employers and jobs are likely to be more varied and more nearly unique than within the larger civil and military meteorological services. Meteorologists often form rather small groups within the business or industrial groups that hire them and even within the universities the meteorology department may be small compared with others. Personal contacts and word-of-mouth advertising at scientific meetings and seminars and maintaining a general awareness of potential openings may prove more useful than the written application as means of getting a job. Meteorology within the private sector is still a rather small profession.

In a university in which the meteorology department is expanding, graduate students who have demonstrated their research or teaching skills may fall naturally into a position on the department staff. The student's advisor or the head of the department may be able to tell him of possible openings at other universities. Universities having departments or courses in meteorology are listed in *Curricula in the Atmospheric Sciences,* a biennial publication of the American Meteorological Society (Chapter 10).

Universities also maintain placement departments where job openings are posted and where arrangements can be made for interviews with representatives of various organizations on recruiting visits. The student should have access to the American Meteorological Society's monthly announcement of job openings and to the professional news journals, noted at the beginning of this chapter, that advertise openings in the atmospheric sciences. A list of the Corporation Members of the American Meteorological Society and the Society's Professional Directory, which appear in each issue of the *Bulletin of the American Meteorological Society,* may offer clues to the airlines and to the industrial, research, and consulting firms that employ meteorologists.

In applying for a job or requesting an interview, it is usual to include with the letter of application a résumé giving the basic information needed by the employer: age, marital status, high school and university, major field, degrees, scholastic standing, work experience, and date available for employment. By duplicating a number of copies of the résumé and including a copy with each letter of application, the job applicant can dispense with much repetitive work and concentrate on composing the letter itself.

PLANNING A CAREER

IN A WORLD in which the best laid plans of mice and men often go awry, it may seem somewhat fatuous to map out a career for oneself. Certainly one cannot map out a schedule for his career; circumstances are sure to alter it. Nevertheless, it helps to have certain broad goals and to have enough self-knowledge to choose the field that, at least potentially, seems to offer the most in personal satisfaction.

In the preceding chapters, we have discussed the various

career areas of meteorology: teaching, research, operations, services, and engineering applications. We have also tried to give an overall view of the kinds of opportunity open to meteorologists in the various fields of employment: the U.S. Civil Service, the Military Services, the universities, and business and industry. At the two extremes, the Civil Service offers maximum stability and security, and running one's own business offers maximum independence. Retirement may come early in the Military Services—an advantage to some individuals who want to make another career, a profound shock to others who find themselves forced to change. One should bear in mind that there is a continual exchange of people between the various meteorological employers as opportunities arise.

A large organization like the National Oceanic and Atmospheric Administration perhaps offers the most varied opportunities to one who is still unsure of the career area best suited to his innate abilities and skills. In trying a number of different areas, the individual often discovers within himself capabilities that neither he nor anyone else suspected were there. It is by doing his best that he learns what he can do, and it is by moving on to new things that he grows. Thus, for some individuals, planning a career is really a lifelong pursuit, a continual matching of newly acquired skills with opportunities.

Planning a career is pretty much up to you.

CHAPTER 10

SCIENTIFIC AND PROFESSIONAL SOCIETIES

MEMBERSHIP IN A SCIENTIFIC and professional society, desirable if not indispensable for the professional scientist in most fields, can be quite useful to the student planning to become a meteorologist. Meeting mature scientists and other professionals at meetings sponsored by the society; furthering his education and, in a sense, his experience through reading the scientific and also the more popularly written publications carrying professional news and similar articles; and help in securing employment—these are a few of the more important benefits the societies offer the student beginning his career in meteorology.

THE AMERICAN METEOROLOGICAL SOCIETY

THE LARGEST PROFESSIONAL and scientific society for meteorologists is the American Meteorological Society with some 8,500 members. Founded in 1919 by Charles F. Brooks (1891-1958), a noted meteorologist associated with Harvard's Blue Hill Observatory, the Society has its Headquarters in

Boston, Mass., and more than eighty local chapters located in the United States and a number of foreign countries. Since its inception, the Society has been associated with the American Association for the Advancement of Science. In 1944-46, during the Presidency of Carl-Gustaf Rossby (Chap. 2), the organization expanded to take on the responsibilities of a professional society in addition to its scientific functions. The reorganization, completed in 1945, provided for the establishment of an Office of Executive Secretary with a full-time paid staff. The objects of the Society, as stated in its Constitution and By-Laws, are *the development and dissemination of knowledge of meteorology in all its phases and applications, and the advancement of its professional ideals.*

To carry out these broad objectives, the American Meteorological Society (AMS) engages in a number of activities. It supports a large-scale publications program that covers the range of scientific, professional, and popular meteorological literature. It sponsors many scientific meetings each year, recognizes career achievement through its membership structure and through annual awards and an undergraduate scholarship, provides educational services, clarifies meteorological problems of public concern, and contributes to the scientific and professional development of its members. These activities, described in more detail below, are carried out by means of an organization that includes elective officials, a Council, five Commissions appointed by the Council, and a relatively small permanent staff.

The elective officers of the Society are the President and a President-Elect. The appointed officers are the Executive Director and the Secretary-Treasurer. The Council, which is the principal governing body of the Society, includes the elective officers, the last two ex-Presidents, and fifteen other members, each elected for a three-year term. The appointed officers are *ex officio* members of the Council. The Council is in general charge of the Society's affairs and is responsible for ensuring that every reasonable action is taken to accomplish its objectives as outlined in the Constitution and By-Laws. An Executive Committee, delegated certain continuing functions by the Council, carries out much of the Society's work. The Executive Director is the head of the permanent staff of the Society and reports to the Executive Committee. The principal operating bodies of the Society in fields other than those delegated to the Executive Committee are the Commissions: these comprise the Commissions on Membership, Publications, Education and Manpower, Scientific and Technological Activities, and Planning. Boards and Committees make up the operating components of the Commissions.

The Society is open to all persons and organizations interested in the atmosphere. The several grades of membership set up by the Constitution are intended to provide opportunities for participation by various groups according to their interests and qualifications. Amateurs and subprofessionals participate as *Associate Members*; this is the grade at which new members ordinarily enter the Society. The category of *Student Member* embraces graduate or undergraduate students at institutions of higher learning who are in residence at least half time. Those considered for election to *Professional Member* must hold a degree, from an institution of higher learning, in meteorology, climatology, or a related discipline and must have served these sciences or their application. In recognition of the interdisciplinary nature of the atmospheric sciences, this educational requirement is interpreted broadly. *Fellows* are individuals who have made outstanding contributions to the science or application of meteorology, climatology, or others area of atmospheric science over a substantial period of years. *Honorary Members* are persons of acknowledged pre-eminence in the field. Corporations and other organizations that wish to support the atmospheric sciences are eligible as candidates for election to *Corporation Member*. The Society recognizes career achievement not only through its grade structure but through annual awards and an undergraduate scholarship.

The AMS publishes three scientific journals, two dealing with basic and applied research in meteorology and one with physical oceanography. The *Bulletin of the American Meteorological Society* is the official organ of the Society and is devoted to editorials, survey articles, professional and membership news, announcements, meeting programs and abstracts, and a professional directory. *Weatherwise* is a bimonthly periodical that has a broad popular appeal for weather amateurs, students, and many subprofessional and professional meteorologists. The Society also publishes certain miscellaneous books, a series of monographs, conference proceedings of the numerous meetings that it sponsors, and a journal of *Meteorological and Geoastrophysical Abstracts*.

In 1970, the Society sponsored or cosponsored 17 national and international meetings. These conferences play a vital role in meteorology by allowing members to exchange information both formally through presented papers and informally through discussions and arguments in hallways, coffee shops, and lounges.

Student Membership, which brings with it four of the Society's five primary periodicals, is particularly useful for the mature student who has already decided on a career in meteorology or a related field. Also of interest to the university student are the local student chapters of the AMS. In 1970, student chapters were located at the City College of New York, Florida State University, Lowell Technical Institute, New York University, the University of Oklahoma, Oregon State University, Pennsylvania State University, Rutgers University, San Jose State College, St. Louis University, Texas A&M University, and the University of Texas.

In Chapter 3, we have already called attention to one of the AMS publications that is highly useful to prospective students of meteorology, *Curricula in the Atmospheric Sciences*. The 1969-1970 Academic Year edition lists the curricula of 58 institutions in the United States and four in Canada. Among the AMS educational programs that are of special value to secondary school and beginning college students interested in a scientific career are the educational monograph and film series. The educational monographs, which survey various topics, such as air pollution, storms, and cloud physics, constitute a series within the *Science Study Series*; the latter was initiated by the Physical Science Studies Committee and is published by Anchor Books, Doubleday & Company, Garden City, New York. Supplementing these popular yet authoritative books is a series of films that use natural, laboratory, analog, or animation photography to illuminate various processes such as the formation of raindrops, nuclei transfer at the sea surface, and solar radiation. These films are distributed commercially. Career guidance articles also appear from time to time in *Weatherwise*—articles, for example, on career opportunities in meteorology, the role of the universities, and high school meteorological curricula, as well as, biennially, selective bibliographies of interest to the amateur and student. The Society also publishes a career guidance pamphlet, *The Challenge of Meteorology,* and prepares mimeographed material on the same subject to answer requests for career information.

Of great potential benefit to those beginning or advancing their careers in the nongovernment sectors of meteorology is the employment service operated by the AMS for the benefit of its members. For a nominal fee, members may subscribe to a monthly announcement of job openings in the fields of private, business, and industrial meteorology and in teaching.

As part of its service to the public and its activity in

A United Airliner captain and first officer discussing the weather in a self-briefing session during flight planning.

advancement of the profession of meteorology, the AMS evaluates radio and television weather programs and grants seals of approval to professional members who conduct their programs in accordance with the set standards. The evaluation is based on the informational value of the program, audience interest, educational value, and the professional attitude of the performer. The Society also operates a certification program for consulting meteorologists; this program evolved out of the rapid growth of the private practice of meteorology after World War II. Still another public service of the AMS is the issuance of policy statements to provide information, in readily understandable form, for the benefit of the general public and of administrative and legislative bodies whose decisions often require sound scientific evidence. Statements are issued in response to a recognized public need for better information on the state of the science and art of meteorology. Finally, to help provide detailed scientific manpower information in the field of atmospheric science, the Society has participated in the preparation of the biennial National Register of Scientific and Technical Personnel (Chapter 8).

Because it provides insight into the ideals and varied working relationships of professional meteorologists, the code of ethics of the American Meteorological Society is reproduced below.

CODE OF ETHICS

In order that the dignity and honor of the meteorological profession my be upheld, that its sphere of usefulness and its contributions to society may be extended, and that meteorologists may be guided as individuals or in association with other meteorologists, the Council of the American Meteorological Society has adopted the following Code of Ethics and Conduct for compliance by the Society's membership:

A. Relationship with the profession as a whole.

1. The meteorologist will endeavor to keep abreast of scientific and technical developments within the profession, and will constantly strive for improvement;

2. He will endeavor to contribute new knowledge to meteorology by making known to the scientific world results of his significant work or research through the media of technical or scientific publications or meetings.

B. Relationship of the meteorologist with his fellow meteorologists.

1. The meteorologist will not engage in unfair competition with other members of his profession;

   a) He will not knowingly solicit another meteorologist's client(s),

   b) He will not interpose between another meteorologist and his prospective client while negotiations or project developments are in progress,

   c) He will attempt to secure work on the basis of qualification and performance, not on lower fees.

2. He will not discredit his fellow meteorologists;

   a) He will not directly or indirectly injure the professional reputation, prospects, or practice of another meteorologist; however, he will present information on unethical, illegal, or unfair practice to the proper authority for action.

   b) He will not review the work of another meteorologist for the same client, except with the other's full knowledge or consent, or unless the association of the other meteorologist has been terminated.

3. He will not take credit knowingly for work done by others; in publications or meetings, he will attempt to give credit where due.

C. Relationship of the meteorologist with his clients and the general public.

1. The meteorologist will base his practice on sound scientific principles applied in a scientific manner;

2. He will not direct his professional activities into practices generally recognized as being detrimental to or incompatible with the general public welfare;

3. He will fully advise his client before undertaking work for compensation as to the probability of success;

4. He will refrain from making exaggerated and unwarranted claims and statements;

   a) Long-range predictions which demonstrate little or no skill over climatology shall be identified as outlooks, experimental predictions, or climatological expectancies, as appropriate.

   b) Stated claims for skill and accuracy of predictions must be based on verification by valid statistical techniques,

   c) General purpose forecasts will not be represented as being adequate for specific operations which are better served by specialized forecasts.

5. He will not use or display the official seal of the American Meteorological Society unless duly authorized by the Society.

6. The meteorologist, regardless of organization affiliation, will refer requests for service which are beyond his professional capabilities or his scope of service to those properly qaulified.

THE AMERICAN GEOPHYSICAL UNION

THE AMERICAN GEOPHYSICAL UNION is a scientific organization that encompasses the disciplines of the physical aspects of the Earth and its environment. In addition to Meteorology, the Union's various Sections include Geodesy; Seismology; Geomagnetism and Paleomagnetism; Oceanography; Volcanology, Geochemistry, and Petrology; Hydrology; Tectonophysics; Planetology; and Solar-Planetary Relationships. The AGU was established in 1919 by the National Research Council of the National Academy of Sciences as the National Committee of the United States for the International Union of Geodesy and Geophysics. Its primary aims are:

1. To promote the study of problems involving the figure (shape) and physics of the Earth and its environment in space;

2. To initiate and coordinate national, international, and interdisciplinary cooperation in research; and

3. To assist and promote discussion and publication of scientific research results.

Thus, the words *interdisciplinary* and *international* characterize the AGU. It draws together scientists from many related disciplines at its national, regional, and international meetings. The Union translates and publishes Russian scientific journals and also has a large publication program of primary journals. The *Journal of Geophysical Research*, published in three sections, covers the broad spectrum of the members' scientific interests, as does the quarterly, *Reviews of Geophysics*. The other two journals, *Water Resources Research* and *Radio Science*, complete the Union's primary publication program. A monthly publication, *EoS*, serves as a medium for articles dealing with the relations between geophysics and society and for semitechnical reviews of currently exciting areas of the science. This popularly written magazine also includes announcements of meetings and new publications, news of people and events, and book reviews of interest to geophysicists, as well as letters and editorials. *EoS* also has a classified section in which "positions available" and "position wanted" are featured. The Union publishes three different book series.

The AGU currently (1970) has about 10,000 members, who may be affiliated with one or more sections of the Union. Members in all categories are elected by the AGU Council, based on the applicants' qualifications and interest in geophysics. *Members* are persons actively engaged in geophysical research or its applications. Progressive experience of three years or more beyond a baccalaureate degree or its equivalent is usually required. *Associates* are persons whose interest in geophysics warrants their election, including the less-experienced person who does not yet qualify for the grade of Member. *Supporting Members* are corporations, other organizations, and individuals interested in geophysics and wishing to support the work of the Union. Of particular interest to readers of this book is the Student Member classification. *Student Members* are college or university students engaged in at least a half-time program of study leading to a degree in science or engineering. All members receive *EoS* and one other AGU periodical (except *Radio Science*), and additional periodicals are at nominal rates; for this purpose, each section of the *Journal of Geophysical Research* is considered one periodical. The three sections treat, essentially, the solid earth, the fluid earth, and space environments. Members also receive a 20 percent discount on books and translated journals ordered for their own use.

Among the Union's professional activities is its awards program. The several awards and medals are made for contributions to fundamental geophysics, unselfish cooperation in research, original research and leadership in certain fields, and significant contributions by a young scientist of outstanding ability.

A graduate meteorology student aspiring to teaching, research, or the management of research would find membership in the AGU a useful affiliation to have. While the American Meteorological Society is the primary professional organization for meteorologists in this country, many in the profession take a leading role in both the AMS and the AGU, and the two organizations hold joint meetings at least once a year. Considering the publications and other benefits that go with student membership, affiliation with both societies could be profitable to the aspiring young scientist.

THE AMERICAN GEOLOGICAL INSTITUTE

THE AMERICAN GEOLOGICAL INSTITUTE is a federation of 17 societies in geology and geophysics. Since the American Geophysical Union is a Member Society of the AGI, members of the Union receive, at nominal cost, the Institute's monthly news magazine, *Geotimes*. *Geotimes* stresses news as distinguished from technical reports and society affairs. Its editorial policy is to serve its readers by presenting impartially any news of Earth scientists and their profession that is likely to affect them. It also publishes semitechnical articles of newsworthy developments in the Earth sciences—to take a specific example, the newly discovered evidence supporting the theory of continental drift—and similar articles. The magazine contains a classified advertising section in which "positions wanted" and vacancies are features.

Because of its educational programs, the AGI and its publications are of particular interest to students considering the teaching of Earth science in the high schools, and also for the training of Earth science teachers. In Chapter 6, we saw that meteorologists at universities may be involved in the training of Earth science secondary school teachers, teaching either regular university courses or courses in the Institutes supported by the National Science Foundation. In the 1960s, the AGI sponsored the Earth Science Curriculum Project, which developed a new integrated science course in which the students are encouraged to discover facts for themselves. The Institute is now sponsoring the Earth Science Teacher Preparation Project, a three-year effort to improve the undergraduate (pre-service) training of prospective teachers. Another AGI-sponsored program is the Environmental Studies Project, which focuses on the need for a radical new approach to science teaching in inner-city public schools.

SELECTED BIBLIOGRAPHY

BOOKS

Atkinson, Bruce W. *The Weather Business: Observation, Analysis, Forecasting and Modification.* New York: Doubleday and Company, Inc., 1969.

Batten, Louis J. *Harvesting the Clouds: Adventures in Weather Modification.* New York: Doubleday and Company, Inc., 1969.

——————. *The Nature of Violent Storms.* New York: Doubleday and Company, 1961.

——————. *Radar Observes the Weather.* New York: Doubleday and Company, 1962.

——————. *The Unclean Sky.* New York: Doubleday and Company, 1966.

Harris, Miles F. *Getting to Know the World Meteorological Organization.* New York: Coward-McCann, Inc., 1966.

Hubert, Lester F., and Paul E. Lehr. *Weather Satellites.* Waltham, Mass.: Blaisdell Publishing Company, 1968.

Hughes, Patrick. *A Century of Weather Service.* New York: Gordon and Breach, 1970.

Landsberg, H. E. *Weather and Health.* New York: Doubleday and Company, Inc., 1969.

Love, Albert, and James Saxon Childers, editors. *Listen to Leaders in Science.* Atlanta: Tupper and Love; New York: David McKay Co., 1965.

Sootin, Harry. *The Long Search: Man Learns about the Nature of Air.* New York: W. W. Norton and Company, Inc., 1967.

PERIODICALS

Bulletin of the American Meteorological Society, published monthly by
the American Meteorological Society, 45 Beacon Street, Boston,
Mass. 02108.

EOS: Transactions, American Geophysical Union, published monthly by
the American Geophysical Union, 2100 Pennsylvania Ave., Washington, D.C. 20037.

NOAA, published quarterly by the National Oceanic and Atmospheric
Administration. U.S. Government Printing Office, Washington, D.C.
20402.

NOAA World, published quarterly by the National Oceanic and Atmo-
pheric Administration. U.S. Government Printing Office, Washington, D.C. 20402.

Weatherwise, published bimonthly by the American Meteorological Society and others, 45 Beacon Street, Boston, Mass. 02108.

Curricula in the Atmospheric Sciences, published biennially by the
American Meteorological Society, 45 Beacon Street, Boston, Mass.
02108.

Occupational Outlook Handbook, published annually by the U.S. Department of Labor. U.S. Government Printing Office, Washington, D.C.
20402.

American Science Manpower, published biennially until 1970-71 by the
National Science Foundation. U.S. Government Printing Office,
Washington, D.C. 20402.

COLLEGES AND UNIVERSITIES
IN THE UNITED STATES AND CANADA
WITH CURRICULA IN ATMOSPHERIC SCIENCE,
1969-1970

Institutions offering both undergraduate and graduate degrees

University of California, Los
　Angeles
Department of Meteorology
Los Angeles, California 90024

University of Chicago
Department of Geophysical
　Sciences
Chicago, Illinois 60637

Cornell University
Department of Agronomy
Ithaca, New York 14850

Drexel Institute of Technology
Department of Physics
Philadelphia, Pennsylvania 19104

Florida State University
Department of Meteorology
Tallahassee, Florida 32306

University of Hawaii
Department of Geosciences
Honolulu, Hawaii 96822

Iowa State University
Department of Earth Science
Ames, Iowa 50010

The University of Kansas
Department of Geography and
　Meteorology
Lawrence, Kansas 66044

The University of Michigan
Department of Meteorology and
　Oceanography
Ann Arbor, Michigan 48104

University of Missouri
Department of Atmospheric
　Science
Columbia, Missouri 65201

Naval Postgraduate School
Department of Meteorology and
　Oceanography
Monterey, California 93940

New Mexico Institute of Mining
　and Technology
Department of Physics and
　Geophysics
Socorro, New Mexico 87801

179

North Carolina State University
Department of Geosciences
Raleigh, North Carolina 27607

The City College of the City
University of New York
Department of Geology and
Physics Department
New York, N.Y. 10031

State University of New York
at Albany
Department of Earth and
Atmospheric Sciences
Albany, New York 12203

New York University
School of Engineering and Science
New York, N.Y. 10453

Northern Illinois University
Department of Earth Sciences
DeKalb, Illinois 60115

The University of Oklahoma
Department of Meteorology
Norman, Oklahoma 73069

The Pennsylvania State University
Department of Meteorology
College of Earth and Mineral
Sciences
University Park, Pa. 16802

Purdue University
Department of Geosciences
Lafayette, Indiana 47907
Rutgers, The State University
of New Jersey

Department of Meteorology
College of Agriculture and
Environmental Science
New Brunswick, N.J. 08903

Saint Louis University
Institute of Technology
St. Louis, Missouri 63156

San Fernando State College
Department of Geography
Northbridge, California 91324

San Jose State College
Department of Meteorology
San Jose, California 95114

Texas A&M University
Department of Meteorology
College Station, Texas 77843

The University of Texas
College of Engineering
Austin, Texas 78712

Utah State University
Department of Soils and
Meteorology
Logan, Utah 84321

University of Utah
Meteorology Department
Salt Lake City, Utah 84112

University of Washington
Department of Atmospheric
Science
Seattle, Washington 98105

University of Wisconsin
Department of Meteorology
Madison, Wisconsin 53706

Massachusetts Institute of
Technology
Department of Meteorology
Cambridge, Massachusetts 02139

McGill University
Department of Meteorology
Montreal 2, Canada

Institutions offering only the undergraduate degree

Bellknap College
Department of Meteorology
Center Harbor, N.H. 03226

University of California, Davis
Department of Agricultural
    Engineering
Davis, California 95616

Lowell Technological Institute
Department of Meteorology
Lowell, Massachusetts 01854

State University of New York
Maritime College
Port Schuyler, New York 10465

State University of New York
Oswego College
Department of Earth Sciences
Oswego, New York 13126

University of St. Thomas
Department of Meteorology
Houston, Texas 77006

Texas Tech University
Department of Geosciences
Lubbock, Texas 79409

Institutions offering only graduate degrees

University of Alaska
Geoscience Department
College, Alaska

University of Arizona
Department of Meteorology
Institute of Atmospheric Physics
Tucson, Arizona 85721

Colorado State University
Department of Atmospheric
    Science
Fort Collins, Colorado 80521

University of Colorado
Department of Astro-Geophysics
Boulder, Colorado 80302

Columbia University
Lamont Geological Observatory
Palisades, New York 10964

University of Denver
College of Engineering
Denver, Colorado 80210

Harvard University
Division of Engineering and
    Applied Physics
Cambridge, Massachusetts 02138

University of Illinois at
    Urbana-Champaign
Urbana, Illinois 61801

The Johns Hopkins University
Department of Earth and
    Planetary Sciences
Baltimore, Maryland 21218

University of Maryland
Institute for Fluid Dynamics and
    Applied Mathematics
College Park, Maryland 20742

University of Missouri-Rolla
Graduate Center for Cloud
   Physics Research
Rolla, Missouri 65401

University of Miami
Institute of Atmospheric Sciences
Coral Gables, Florida 33124

University of Minnesota
School of Physics and Astronomy
Minneapolis, Minnesota 55455

University of Nevada
Department of Physics
Reno, Nevada 89507

Oregon State University
Department of Atmospheric
   Sciences
Corvallis, Oregon 97331

Princeton University
Program in Geophysical Fluid
   Dynamics
Princeton, New Jersey 08540

South Dakota School of Mines
   and Technology
Department of Meteorology
Rapid City, South Dakota 57701

University of Wisconsin,
   Milwaukee
College of Letters and Science
Milwaukee, Wisconsin 53201

University of Wyoming
College of Engineering
Laramie, Wyoming

Yale University
Interdisciplinary Proagrm in
   Biometeorology
New Haven, Connecticut 06511

The University of Alberta
Department of Geography
Edmonton, Alberta

University of Toronto
Department of Physics
Toronto, Ontario

University of Waterloo
Department of Mechanical
   Engineering
Waterloo, Ontario

INDEX